PIPE FITTINGS

Y0-ABL-940

 NIPPLES

 PIPE LENGTHS UP TO 22 FT.

 STRAIGHT COUPLING

 REDUCING COUPLING

 COUPLING

 NUT

CAP

 STRAIGHT TEE

 REDUCING TEE

 STREET TEE

 STRAIGHT CROSS

 REDUCING CROSS

90° ELBOW

90° ELBOW

 90° ELBOW

 45° ELBOW

 REDUCING ELBOW

 90° STREET ELBOW

45° STREET ELBOW

 45° Y-BEND

 REDUCING TEE

 REDUCER

UNION (3 PARTS) PLUG BUSHING CAP RETURN BEND

90°   45°   STREET
UNION ELBOWS

UNION TEES

 PLUG

45° ELBOW

 TEE

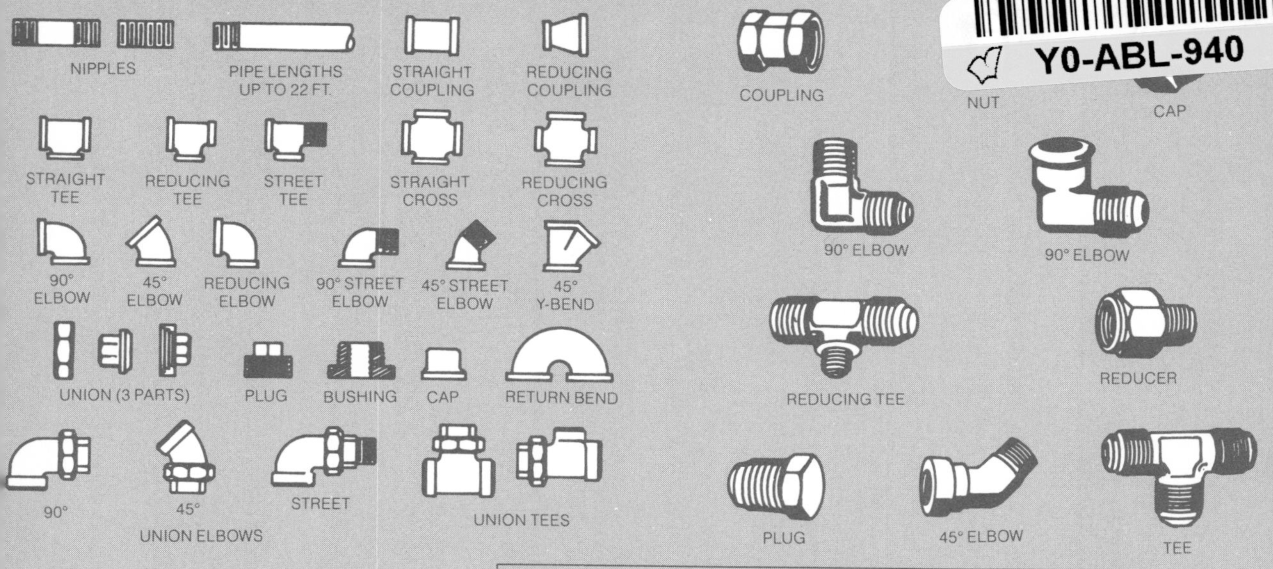

MEASURES OF CAPACITY

1 cup	= 8 fl oz
2 cups	= 1 pint
2 pints	= 1 quart
4 quarts	= 1 gallon
2 gallons	= 1 peck
4 pecks	= 1 bushel

STANDARD STEEL PIPE ((All Dimensions in inches)

Nominal Size	Outside Diameter	Inside Diameter	Nominal Size	Outside Diameter	Inside Diameter
⅛	0.405	0.269	1	1.315	1.049
¼	0.540	0.364	1¼	1.660	1.380
⅜	0.675	0.493	1½	1.900	1.610
½	0.840	0.622	2	2.375	2.067
¾	1.050	0.824	2½	2.875	2.469

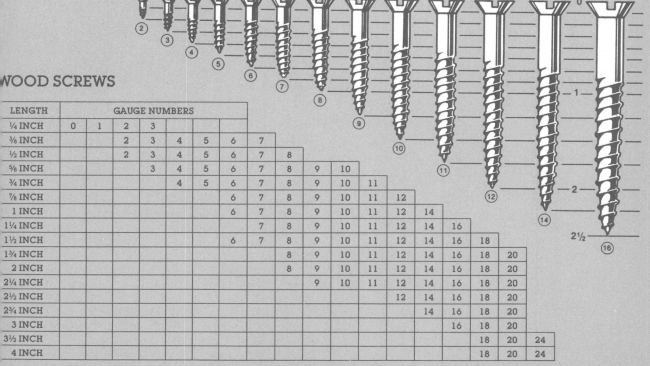

WOOD SCREWS

LENGTH	GAUGE NUMBERS														
¼ INCH	0	1	2	3											
⅜ INCH			2	3	4	5	6	7							
½ INCH			2	3	4	5	6	7	8						
⅝ INCH				3	4	5	6	7	8	9	10				
¾ INCH					4	5	6	7	8	9	10	11			
⅞ INCH							6	7	8	9	10	11	12		
1 INCH							6	7	8	9	10	11	12	14	
1¼ INCH								7	8	9	10	11	12	14	16
1½ INCH						6	7	8	9	10	11	12	14	16	18
1¾ INCH								8	9	10	11	12	14	16	18	20
2 INCH								8	9	10	11	12	14	16	18	20
2¼ INCH									9	10	11	12	14	16	18	20
2½ INCH											12	14	16	18	20
2¾ INCH												14	16	18	20
3 INCH													16	18	20
3½ INCH														18	20	24
4 INCH														18	20	24

WHEN YOU BUY SCREWS, SPECIFY (1) LENGTH, (2) GAUGE NUMBER, (3) TYPE OF HEAD—FLAT, ROUND, OR OVAL, (4) MATERIAL—STEEL, BRASS, BRONZE, ETC., (5) FINISH—BRIGHT, STEEL BLUED, CADMIUM, NICKEL, OR CHROMIUM PLATED.

Popular Mechanics

do-it-yourself encyclopedia

The complete, illustrated home reference guide from the world's most authoritative source for today's how-to-do-it information.

Volume 24

TILE
to
TRACTORS

HEARST DIRECT BOOKS

NEW YORK

Acknowledgements

The Popular Mechanics Encyclopedia is published with the consent and cooperation of POPULAR MECHANICS Magazine.

For POPULAR MECHANICS Magazine:

Editor-in-Chief: *Joe Oldham*

Managing Editor: *Bill Hartford*

Special Features Editor: *Sheldon M. Gallager*

Automotive Editor: *Wade A. Hoyt, SAE*

Home and Shop Editor: *Steve Willson*

Electronics Editor: *Stephen A. Booth*

Boating, Outdoors and Travel Editor: *Timothy H. Cole*

Science Editor: *Dennis Eskow*

Popular Mechanics Encyclopedia

Project Director: *Boyd Griffin*

Manufacturing: *Ron Schoenfeld*

Assistant Editors: *Cynthia W. Lockhart*
Peter McCann, Rosanna Petruccio

Production Coordinator: *Peter McCann*

The staff of Popular Mechanics Encyclopedia is grateful to the following individuals and organizations:

Editor: *C. Edward Cavert*

Editor Emeritus: *Clifford B. Hicks*

Production: *Layla Productions*

Production Director: *Lori Stein*

Book Design: *The Bentwood Studio*

Art Director: *Jos. Trautwein*

Design Consultant: *Suzanne Bennett & Associates*

Illustrations: *AP Graphics, Evelyne Johnson Associates, Popular Mechanics Magazine, Vantage Art.*

Contributing Writers: Dave Acton, *Toy dump truck*, page 3061, H. R. Haggerty, *Toy plane for mini-pilots*, page 3062; Len Hilts, *Floor tile basics*, page 2948, *Wall tile basics.* page 2957, Terence E. Hogan, *Kitchen appliance for your youngster*, page 3058, G. R. Jobe, *Garden tractor trailer*, page 3068, Elmer J. Loiselle, *Scooters from skates*, page 3053, Maurice Orlarey, *Hydraulic lift for your tractor*, page 3064, Pat Perret, *Trailer your boat*, page 3025, Merton H. Slutz, *Buzzing bumblebees*, page 3032, Elma Waltner *Ducks and Dachshunds That Talk*, page 3033, Elma and Williard Waltner, *Pulltoy circus train*, page 3054, Williard Waltner *Fleet of blockmobiles*, page 3029, David Warren and William Beyer, *Work wonders with tile*, page 2951, Harry Wicks, *Tool box classics you can build.* page 3009, C. L. Widdicombe, *You haul toy car* page 3063.

Picture Credits: Popular Mechanics Encyclopedia is grateful to the following for permission to reprint their photographs: Cox Trailers, Inc., pages 3025 and 3026; Dremel Co., page 2986 (top); Don Geary, page 2974; George Retseck, pages 2969 (top, center, bottom), 3022 (top); Sears Roebuck and Co., pages 2977 (top and bottom), 2981 (top left), 2983 (top right and bottom right), 2984 (left and right), and 2985 (left and right); Skil Corp., 2982 (top and bottom), 2983 (left), and 2986 (bottom); Stanley Tools, a Division of the Stanley Works, pages 2975, 2976 (left and right), 2978, 2979 (left and right), 2980 (left and right), and 2981 (bottom left and right).

ISBN 0-87851-177-6

Library of Congress 85-81760

10 9 8 7 6 5 4 3

PRINTED IN THE UNITED STATES OF AMERICA

Although every effort has been made to ensure the accuracy and completeness of the information in this book, Hearst Direct Books makes no guarantees, stated or implied, nor will they be liable in the event of misinterpretation or human error made by the reader, or for any typographical errors that may appear. WORK SAFELY WITH HAND TOOLS. WEAR SAFETY GOGGLES. READ MANUFACTURER'S INSTRUCTIONS AND WARNINGS FOR ALL PRODUCTS.

Contents

VINYL FLOOR TILES faithfully simulate brick, wood and other surfaces yet are easier to maintain.

ANYTHING BUT DRAB, vinyl floor patterns can accent the motif of any room.

Floor tile basics

■ THE MOST DIFFICULT part of laying a new tile floor is deciding which tile pattern you like best. The stores and home centers which sell vinyl flooring have such a wide range of colors and designs that you'll probably need several hours for browsing and choosing.

Vinyl and vinyl-asbestos tiles are the most popular types of do-it-yourself floors. Most rooms can be floored with them in a day, or at most a weekend. Best of all, vinyls offer no-wax finishes so you can put down a floor that is both beautiful and free of upkeep.

You'll find two basic varieties of resilient tiles: self-adhesive and dry-back. With the self-adhesive, just peel off a backing paper, place the tile in position on the floor, and press it down. With the dry-backs, you first apply an adhesive to the floor.

Selecting the tile

Which kind to use? Because they are easier to use, most people now prefer the self-adhesive vinyl tiles. But your choice may be determined by other factors, such as pattern or price.

All-vinyl tiles are relatively soft, have embossed surfaces, and are offered in an incredible selection of designs. Vinyl-asbestos tiles are harder, a little thicker, have smooth surfaces, and are not available in as many designs. The design goes clear through the tile so that wear doesn't show for a long time. Vinyls may have a no-wax finish, while vinyl-asbestos tiles need an occasional waxing.

If you need long service in a high traffic area, opt for the vinyl-asbestos. It often is used in stores and offices. You may find some with self-adhesive backs, though most are dry.

If you want a wide selection of patterns, a no-wax finish and easy installation, then choose the embossed vinyl styles. You may have to replace them sooner than vinyl-asbestos but they are easy to take up and replace.

Preparation

Good preparation is the secret of laying any floor covering. The basic rules are these:

1. The subfloor must be level and smooth. Any bump in the subfloor soon will show up as a bump in the tile, and that bump will wear rapidly.

Some homeowners lay new tiles directly on existing tile floors. If the old tile is sound and smooth, this is all right, but examine the old floor before you do it. Wear may have made it uneven. Any imperfections in the old floor will quickly appear in the new floor. If in doubt, take up the old tiles.

2. The subfloor must be dry and free of dust. Dust interferes with any adhesive but especially the adhesive on self-sticking tiles. Vacuum the floor just before you lay new tiles.

3. Plan your layout with care so that the tiles align properly.

4. With concrete floors, notably basement floors below grade, you not only may have dust, but often a moisture problem as well. Moisture may seep slowly up through the slab. In past years, asphalt cement adhesive was used to lay tiles below grade, and only asphalt tiles were used. Now a vinyl floor sealer can be brushed on to provide a thick coating which seals out both moisture and dust. This permits the use of most types of floor tile below grade.

Removing the old floor

When taking up an old tile floor, remove all traces of tile, old lining felt and adhesive. *Do not sand old flooring materials to remove them.* Many were made with asbestos fibers; the dust may contain asbestos particles and be very hazardous to your health. Remove old tiles by pulling up and scraping. Dispose of the old material in heavy-duty plastic bags, tied shut and marked, "Caution—contains asbestos. Dispose in an approved landfill only."

If the felt sticks to the subfloor, remove it by wetting—not soaking—and then scraping. Scrubbing the dampened felt with a stiff brush helps in difficult cases. Asphalt solvent will remove any old adhesive.

Once all the old stuff is off the floor, check the surface. If it isn't flat and smooth, take the time to level it now. You'll get a much better final result.

Leveling the subfloor

If you are tiling a wood floor, the best way to achieve a smooth subfloor is to nail underlayment over the surface. You can buy hardboard sheets made for this purpose at your home center. All nailheads must be flush with the surface.

You can fill low spots in concrete floors with leveling compounds available at tile stores (usually latex cement mixtures), taking care to bring the low spot just up to the level of the rest of the floor and to feather the edges of the patch.

To level slight depressions in a concrete floor

or to smooth out rough surfaces, you can brush several coats of the vinyl sealer on low areas. This seals the floor against moisture and dust and provides a level, smooth surface for both dry-backed and adhesive-backed tiles.

Finally, pry away any molding at the walls. This molding should be replaced after the new floor is down.

Floor layout

Mark your floor with guidelines before cementing tiles down. To do this, find the center points on two opposite walls and strike a chalk line across the floor from one to the other. Measure this line and place a tile at the midpoint, as shown in the drawing, to establish a perpendicular line.

Extend this line to both walls, thus dividing the room into quarters. Next, place tiles temporarily along these lines from the center of the room to the side walls. At this point you may want to move one or both lines slightly to avoid cutting narrow strips along the walls.

Placing the tiles

If installing self-adhesive tiles, strip the release paper from one tile and place the tile at the point where the lines cross in the center of the room. Before putting the tile down, turn it over. Some brands have arrows printed on the back. Install all tiles with the arrows running in the same direction. Be sure to align the sides of the tile with the chalk lines. Strip a second tile and butt it against the first, and also align it with the chalk line.

The placement of these first tiles is vitally important because if they don't line up, all others also will be misaligned. After positioning a tile, press it firmly in place. Continue putting tiles down until the floor is covered. The final job is to cut tiles to fit the spaces at the base of the walls.

If you are installing dry-backed tiles, you will use a canned adhesive. Read the instructions on the label before applying it, and follow them exactly. Adhesives differ; instructions vary from brand to brand. Most call for application with a notched adhesive spreader, but some adhesives are brushed on. Most are applied to a section of floor at a time, and require a short drying time before the tile is applied.

When the adhesive has set, place a tile at the point where the chalk lines cross. Don't slide the tile into place. Instead, place one side accurately on the chalk line and snap the other side down. You can slide the tile a little for accurate placement, but if you move it too much, you may disturb the adhesive. Place a second tile against the first and snap it into place. Be certain the tiles butt accurately. Continue until the floor is finished except for the areas at the base of the wall.

Cutting tiles

Soft vinyl tiles can be cut with a utility knife or heavy scissors. Harder vinyl asbestos tiles are scored deeply with a utility knife, then snapped along the score line. Place the tile on a table with the score line along the table edge, then snap sharply down on the part of the tile extending beyond the table.

To cut tiles to fit at the base of the wall, place a loose tile over the last full tile in a row. Place another tile on top of this and slide this tile toward the wall until it touches the wall. Use the edge of this tile as a guide and draw a line on the tile beneath it, as shown in the drawing. When you cut along this line, the cut tile will fit exactly into the space at the base of the wall.

To make irregular cutouts to fit around pipes and other obstructions, draw a paper pattern of the cutout. Trace this on the tile and cut it out with a utility knife.

With the last tile installed, just move the furniture back into place and start enjoying your new floor.

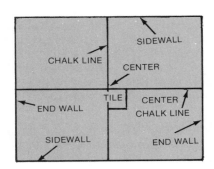

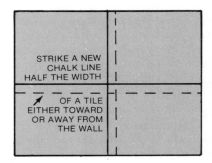

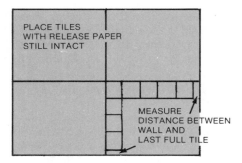

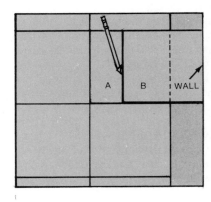

1. To begin floor layout, find the center between opposite walls, and strike a chalk line across the room. This is the "center chalk line." Next, locate the center of this line. Place a tile, as shown, at the center point and use it to draw a chalk line perpendicular to the first line. The floor is now divided into quarters.

2. Place a row of tiles along the perpendicular chalk line from the center of the room to the sidewall. Do not remove release paper. Measure distance from last tile to wall.

3. If space from last tile to the wall is less than half the width of a tile, strike a new chalk line beside old center line. Make it half the width of a tile on either side (your choice) of old center line. This provides even borders on both sides of the room.

4. To measure tile to fit space at base of wall, place a loose tile exactly on top of last full tile in any row. Place third tile on top of this and slide it until it contacts wall. Use edge of tile as a guide to mark the tile under it with a pencil. Cut along this line with heavy-duty scissors or utility knife.

Work wonders with tile

■ SOME DO-IT-YOURSELFERS shy away from ceramic tile because they think it's too difficult to work with. This was true years ago, when tiles had to be set in a thick mortar. Today, however, pre-spaced sheeting and new, easy-to-apply adhesives make setting tile relatively simple.

Tools and equipment

A few specialized tools are needed to lay ceramic tile. They are usually available through the tile dealer or at a local rental shop. They include a tile cutter or glass cutter, tile nippers, hacksaw

with a rod saw blade, notched trowel, rubber float and squeegee.

You probably have the basic tools that are also required: chalkline, plumb line, carpenter's level, square, Carborundum stone and putty knife. Professional tile people sometimes use a power saw with a diamond blade to cut tile. This can be rented with the other specialized tools.

TECHNIQUE OF FRAMING a square of tiles, then filling in the square, helps to keep the tiles straight and evenly spaced.

A TILE CUTTER is one special tool you'll need. It makes straight cuts. Pull the handle backward to score the tile, then press down to break it at the score.

A measuring stick of lattice stock made for the size of the tile you are setting is a handy tool. Mark off tile widths, alternating with ¼-in. grout spaces over the length of the stick. If you're using sheeted tiles, mark the width of a sheet and leave the same space between sheet marks as exists between tiles on a sheet.

Use the measuring stick to determine the approximate number of tiles you'll need to do a floor, wall or kitchen countertop. You'll have some breakage, so add about 5 percent more. Some dealers will give you a refund for unused tile. Check before you buy.

Ceramic tiles come in many shapes, colors, designs and textures. They are used indoors and outdoors, on floors, walls and fireplaces, as solid surfaces or as borders. Ceramic tiles come glazed or unglazed. Quarry tiles are a type of unglazed tile.

Tiles less than 4¼ in. square are usually mounted on sheets, with all tiles properly spaced. You just have to make sure the space between the sheets matches the space between the tiles.

Ceramic tiles 4¼ in. and larger are usually set individually. Some have built-in spacers that are covered when grout is applied. Other large tiles must be spaced visually or with separate spacers shaped like small plus signs positioned at each tile corner. Remove them when the mortar has set sufficiently. You can also use thin plywood strips as temporary spacers.

Adhesives and grout

Ceramic tiles are held in place by adhesives. Traditionally, tiles were held by a mortar bed. Today, there are adhesives that are much easier to use. They fall into three categories: organic-based, cement-based and epoxy-based. The kind you use depends on the kind of tile, the type of subsurface, the location of the tile installation, and the area to be tiled—a wall or a floor. Read the label on the can and check with the tile dealer to be sure the adhesive is suitable.

Organic adhesives, also called mastics, are of two types. Type I is water-resistant for use in damp areas, and type II is for dry areas.

Cement-based adhesives are also of two types. One is a Portland cement base mixed with a latex additive. The other is a dry-set mortar that's mixed with water. Both can be used on concrete slabs. With an additive, the first type is used on wood.

Epoxy adhesive provides a strong bond over plywood, concrete, wallboard and ceramic tile. Use it outdoors.

Grout is the substance applied to fill spaces between tiles after the tiles are laid. The three common types of grout are cement-based, silicone rubber-based and epoxy-based. Cement-based grout is most commonly used by professionals and do-it-yourselfers. Epoxy-based grout should be used when epoxy adhesive is used. Grout comes in many colors to match the tile. Grout can come premixed or as a powder that requires mixing.

Unglazed tile and tile that has been grouted with cement-based grout should be sealed. A silicone-based sealer is best for use in wet areas.

Ceramic tile for a floor

If you're applying ceramic tile to a floor, preparing the surface beneath the tile is the key. If you're laying tiles on a wood floor, be sure there are no protruding nails, that all boards are nailed down tightly and that the floor is level, with no raised board edges.

Do not try to lay ceramic tile directly on a floor covered with resilient flooring, "no-wax" tile or urethane-coated flooring. A resilient underlayment will crack the grout and loosen the tiles. A no-wax floor covering will produce a weak bond with the adhesive.

If you must lay tile atop these materials, nail ¼-in. plywood or underlayment-grade hardboard over the floor to provide a base for the tile. Stagger the joints, nailing at least every 6 in. in the center and every 3 in. around the outside edges with 6d ring shank nails. Set all nails.

This quarry tile floor was laid on a new concrete floor and on a new patio. To provide a strong, durable bond both inside and out, a three-part epoxy-based adhesive mix was used. Two liquids are mixed, and then a powder is added. The amount mixed should be limited for use in 20 to 30 minutes. This adhesive will set in 45 minutes to 1½ hours, depending on the temperature. If you're laying tile outside, the temperature should be at least 45 °F. Remember, the lower the temperature, the longer the setting time.

When you're ready to begin the installation, measure and mark the center points of two facing walls and snap a chalkline between them. Snap a chalkline at center points of the other walls after checking with a carpenter's square to be sure the lines are at right angles to each other.

As a test, place a row of tiles from the center to the wall along one line. If the last tile is less than half-width, readjust the other line. Then continue using the chalkline to divide the floor into squares that will encompass anywhere from 9 to 12 tiles, starting at the center of the room.

Apply adhesive inside these squares and up to but not covering the chalklines. Be sure to use the trowel recommended on the label. Work on two or three squares at a time. Set tiles along the lines to form a square frame, then fill in the remaining space. Set tiles in place with a slight twist—don't slide them.

Good contact

Test the first tile you set by putting it in position, pressing it firmly, then lifting it off to see if good overall contact has been made with the adhesive. This will help determine whether you are applying enough adhesive.

Don't allow the adhesive to develop a dry film or the tiles won't adhere properly. Take care to space the tiles evenly if they have no built-in spacers. Forming squares helps to visually align and space the tiles.

Cut the edge tiles with a tile cutter. To make a straight cut in a tile, use a tile cutter to score the tile, then break it along the score. You can also use a metal straightedge and glass cutter to score the tile. To break it along the score, lay the tile over a finishing nail or coat hanger wire and press down on the edges.

To shape a tile, use nippers to chip away small bites until the desired shape is achieved. Snap away about ⅛ in. at a time. Larger bites may break the tile. You can also use a rod saw to cut rounded shapes or enlarge holes started with a masonry drill bit. Finish a quarter of the room before proceeding to the next section. Always use protective eyewear when cutting ceramic tile.

Wait at least 24 hours before applying grout. If you use a dry grout mix, prepare only enough for 10 or 15 minutes of work. Let it stand for about 10 minutes after mixing, then remix. Wear rubber gloves when mixing and applying grout to avoid skin irritation.

How to apply grout

Apply the grout with a rubber-faced float. Be sure the spaces between the tiles are tightly packed. Go over each area two or three times to be certain the grout is packed into the joints.

Wipe off excess grout by drawing a squeegee diagonally across the grout lines. Remove as much excess as possible to reduce the cleaning effort later. This is particularly important with quarry tile, since it is porous. You can prevent a thin film of grout from remaining on the surface of quarry tile if you apply a grout-release product before grouting. Follow the instructions carefully regarding removal time.

Allow 15 to 20 minutes for the grout to set, then clean the tile surfaces with a damp sponge. After about 30 minutes, polish the surfaces with a coarse, dry cloth. When the grout has cured for 72 hours, brush on two coats of silicone sealer to make the grout resistant to water and soiling. Wait one hour between coats and rub the tile with a clean cloth after the second coat to restore luster.

Installing a ceramic tile backsplash

Tiling a kitchen backsplash is a good introductory tile project. With careful attention, you should be able to align tiles in the limited space.

Wall preparation is important. Patch holes left from relocating light switches, electrical outlets or telephone jacks. Fill the wall space beyond the hole with fiberglass insulating material. Then gently press spackle into the hole with a putty knife. Overfill slightly to allow for shrinkage. When the spackle is dry, sand it flush with the wall.

You don't have to fill small nail holes unless the plaster or drywall surrounding them is broken or loose. In such a case, remove the loose material and patch the area. Remove wallpaper before tiling. Old wallpaper can come loose and cause the tile to sag.

When the backsplash area is ready for tile adhesive, mark a base line and a plumb line at the starting point. When working on a kitchen backsplash, you can use the top of the counter as a base line if it is relatively level. In a limited area such as this, where the top edge of the tile will be concealed below wall cabinets, slight variations along the base line can be taken up by the grout space.

Test-lay a full row or sheet of tile across the width of the wall. If one of the end tiles is less than ½ in. wide, remove a tile.

Most tile adhesives set up in 15 to 45 minutes, depending on the temperature. It's best to work a small area at a time. Use a 5/16-in. V-notched trowel to spread mastic for most ceramic wall tile sizes. If you are using ceramic tiles that are 9 to 12 in. square, use a ¼-in. square-notched trowel. Hold the trowel at 45° while applying the adhesive.

When working around a kitchen backsplash, bathtub or shower where water will be splashed onto the wall, apply a skim coat of adhesive with the flat edge of the trowel. Let this dry, then apply a coat with the notched side for setting the tiles. The double coat will help waterproof the area.

While applying the skim coat, you can also pack cracks between the countertop and wall so water cannot seep in.

When you need individual tiles to fit around light switches or other openings, peel sheet tiles from their backing. Make straight cuts with a tile cutter and make shaped cuts with tile nippers, a rod saw or a masonry drill bit.

At one or both ends of the backsplash, you will probably have to cut tiles to fit. Since most walls are not plumb, cut end tiles as you work, to ensure a good fit. Allow space for grout when cutting partial tiles.

After the wall has been tiled for about 24 hours, apply grout to fill the spaces between tiles.

Follow the procedure discussed for grouting quarry tile, mixing only enough grout for 10 to 15 minutes of work. Allow it to stand for 10 minutes before remixing. Spread the grout with a rubber float. Then use the edge of the float or a squeegee to clean away as much as possible from the surface.

After 15 to 20 minutes, clean the tile surface with a damp sponge. After 30 minutes, polish the surface with a cloth; and after 72 hours, seal the backsplash with two coats of silicone sealer.

Entry floor that won't wear out

■ IF YOU HAVE wood floors, there are probably a few spots that are dull and worn. This is most likely to happen just inside your front or back door where traffic is heaviest. These areas take the worst beating in bad weather because they're the principal targets of muddy shoes, snow-covered boots and dripping raincoats. Quarry tile can provide a long-term solution. It's available in good-looking colors and a varied selection of sizes and patterns.

No matter which setting system you use, prepare the job by thoroughly cleaning the subfloor and squaring up your layout to minimize any cutting. Most tile suppliers have cutters and chippers that you can rent to avoid buying the tools for a one-shot job. Here's a rundown of the different applications that will give you a solid, long-lasting job.

Application over concrete

Organic adhesive is a prepared material that comes in tubes or cans and is usually applied with a notched trowel. This method is clean, fast, and gives you flexibility in correcting tile placement. *Read the label cautions.* Most recommend thorough ventilation during use; some are flammable and their solvents may cause skin irritation. The recommended grout is a 1:2 ratio of

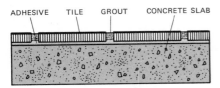

ADHESIVE   TILE   GROUT   CONCRETE SLAB

ORGANIC ADHESIVE

portland cement and sand. It should be wet-cured by covering the entire floor with polyethylene sheeting for three days. Water is spread on the surface the second day and the sheet replaced.

Cement mortar is a mixture of portland cement and sand in the proportion of 1:6. The mortar can be reinforced with metal lath or mesh.

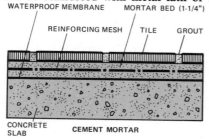

This installation can withstand prolonged contact with water. The thickness of the bed (¾ to 1¼ inches) gives you enough room to compensate for depressed or irregular areas. Use the same 1:2 cement-to-sand ratio for grout.

Application over wood

Organic adhesive is ideal here, too. Many homeowners are already familiar with this process because it is similar to installing vinyl tile. The recommended grout over a wood subfloor is latex-portland cement. The latex additive makes

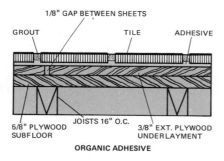

it less rigid than regular cement grout. The Tile Council of America sets standards calling for a ⅝-inch plywood subfloor and a ⅜-inch exterior-grade plywood underlayment.

Epoxy adhesive combines resins and hardeners to provide high bond strength. It is recommended for renovations where ceramic tile is to be installed over existing resilient tile. This eliminates the need for a new layer of plywood. A latex-portland cement grout should be used.

The installation methods detailed above are rated for residential and light industrial use. There are even more elaborate procedures (although you won't need them) that use chemically resistant mortar on an acid-proof membrane that can withstand 300-pound loads on steel wheels as

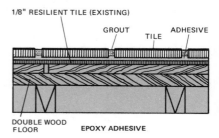

well as severe chemical exposure. Durability and low maintenance are the qualities that make ceramic tile more desirable than resilient tile. For these reasons, all the platforms built for the new rapid transit system in Washington, D.C., are of ceramic tile. So don't worry when the kids come home covered with mud or snow—your quarry-tile floor can take it.

AS SHOWN at right, quarry tile comes in several sizes and patterns. Matching trim is available for edges and corners.

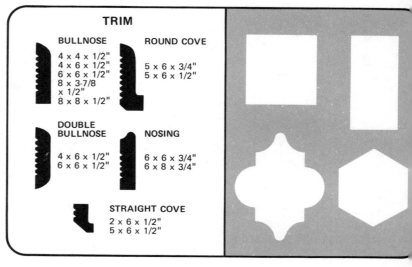

TRIM

BULLNOSE
4 x 4 x 1/2"
4 x 6 x 1/2"
6 x 6 x 1/2"
8 x 3-7/8 x 1/2"
8 x 8 x 1/2"

ROUND COVE
5 x 6 x 3/4"
5 x 6 x 1/2"

DOUBLE BULLNOSE
4 x 6 x 1/2"
6 x 6 x 1/2"

NOSING
6 x 6 x 3/4"
6 x 8 x 3/4"

STRAIGHT COVE
2 x 6 x 1/2"
5 x 6 x 1/2"

Wall tile basics

■ TILE ADDS THE FINISHING TOUCH to a house. It is both pleasing to the eye and practical in bathrooms, kitchens and even as a part of the decorative motif in living rooms. Add to that the fact that you can now tile any area yourself, and tile becomes an important material for the homeowner to know about.

Here are some of the ways you can use tile in your home to increase its livability and, incidentally, to increase its sale value:

1. *Bathrooms*. Tile the tub enclosure all the way to the ceiling. Tile the area above and back of the sink as a backsplash. Tile all the walls to chair-rail height, or tile the entire wall area. Tile the floor. Whether you do a lot or a little, new tile will make the bathroom easier to care for and better to look at.

2. *Powder rooms*. As a rule, powder rooms (half baths) have less tiled area than bathrooms, with the majority of the wall area painted or wallpapered. However, if you choose, you can tile the whole thing, including the floor. At a minimum, you can install a tile backsplash for the sink.

3. *Laundry room*. Tile behind the laundry machines and the laundry sink can really add a touch of class to the usually plebian laundry room. If your laundry area is in the basement, tile on those gray concrete walls will dramatically elevate the appearance of the place.

4. *Kitchen*. You can tile your counters here if you choose, but the usual use of tile in the kitchen is on the walls between the cabinet bottoms and the countertops, and as a backsplash for the sink. You can, of course, tile the floor but keep in mind that tile when wet can be slippery. Vinyl floor tiles with a nonslip surface would probably be more practical here than ceramic tiles.

5. *Living areas*. If you are looking for a way to create a distinctive living area, think about using tile, especially small mosaic tile, on one wall. There is a wide array of colors in a variety of shapes available, so you can really employ your imagination in designing this wall. Obviously, you can do too much tiling, too. Think about doing one wall or even a section of one wall. If you have a fireplace that seems a bit humdrum, you might tile the wall above or around it for a new effect.

6. *Much-used areas*. Take a tip from the people who design public buildings if you have an area such as a long hall which is constantly in need of painting or washing because of fingerprints. You can cut the maintenance of such areas by tiling the lower, most-soiled portion. Don't use stark white bathroom tiles for this. Achieve a decorative effect by using colorful, small mosaic tiles.

Types of tile

There are three basic types of wall tile—ceramic, metal and plastic. Plastic tile is consid-

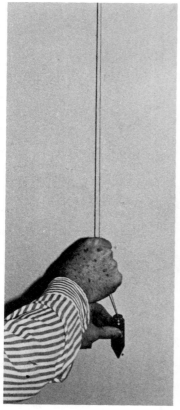

DROP a chalked plumb line and snap it to make a vertical guide.

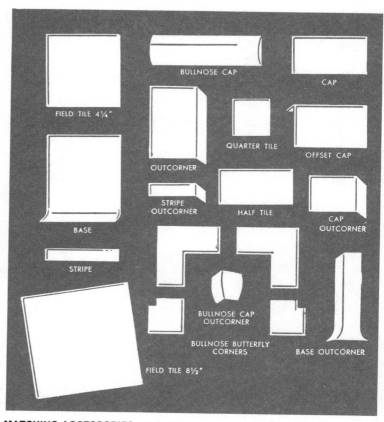

BULLNOSE CAP

CAP

FIELD TILE 4¼"

QUARTER TILE

OFFSET CAP

OUTCORNER

STRIPE OUTCORNER

HALF TILE

CAP OUTCORNER

BASE

STRIPE

BULLNOSE CAP OUTCORNER

BULLNOSE BUTTERFLY CORNERS

BASE OUTCORNER

FIELD TILE 8½"

MATCHING ACCESSORIES are available with all types of tile. These include bases, caps, soap dishes, glass holders, towel bars and tissue holders.

TILES ALSO COME in a variety of novelty shapes and sizes, including the small mosaic variety. You can use these for both walls and floors.

erably less expensive than ceramic tile, and is easier to install because cutting the plastic is easier than cutting the ceramic. But you pay a penalty because plastic tile tends to scratch easily in areas of heavy use. When scratched, it loses its luster. Also, some of the colored plastic fades with age. Metal tile is enameled, and its colors also tend to fade.

Ceramic tile, on the other hand, maintains its appearance under very heavy wear and does not fade. Its hard surface resists penetration of all types of dirt and grime. The surface of the grout between the tiles can get dirty and can become mildewed, however, so you need a regular cleaning program to keep the tile looking good.

Realtors tend to put a higher value on homes with ceramic tile baths, so keep this in mind as you make your decision. A larger expenditure now may mean a better price later.

The basic tile size is 4¼ x 4¼-in. Both plastic and ceramic tile are produced in this size. You can also find tiles up to 8½ x 8½-in. sq., but these usually are special-order items, while the standard sizes can now be purchased at most home center stores and from major mail-order houses.

In addition to the square field tiles, you can purchase a number of special shapes, including several different shapes of base and cap pieces. See the accompanying illustration. When planning your tiling job, make a list of the number of field tiles and of special shapes you will need. In addition to the shapes shown, you can also buy tile towel bars, toilet tissue holders, and soap dishes, all of which attach directly to the wall with tile mastic.

Tiles in decorative shapes have become available, too. With these, you can get away from the "standard" tile look and create exceptionally attractive tiled areas. Lozenge shapes, for example, provide a very Spanish look. These unusual tiles are no more difficult to install than the square units.

You can also buy small tiles, down to as small as half an inch square. These smaller tiles, called mosaics, come in square-foot sheets, with the tiles cemented to a mesh backing. Thus, you don't have to lay each tiny tile individually, but can put the tile up a square foot at a time. You'll find these mosaic tiles available in many colors, in sheets with multicolors on them, and even sheets with special designs already created.

If you are thinking about tiling any area in your home, the best way to start is to visit a couple of local home centers to see which types are readily available. Just looking at the tile displays will give you some ideas on how to use these fine home additions.

The mastic

Tiles are glued in place with a special mastic which you buy in large cans. The mastic is applied to the wall with a toothed spreader which leaves tiny ridges of mastic of just the right height. This prevents you from putting too much mastic on, and makes for a neat final job. If you apply too much mastic it will squeeze out between the tiles and mar the new surface.

Modern square tiles have another built-in solution to an old problem. Each tile has small spacers on all four edges. Thus, when you put the tile in place on the wall, you butt it up against its neighbor without worrying about how much space to leave between the two. The spacers on the tiles will automatically provide the correct spacing.

Cutting tile to fit

Many people have shied away from putting up their own tile, especially ceramic tile, because they have heard that cutting and trimming tile is difficult—a job for a professional. This isn't true. Cutting tile is similar to, but easier than, cutting glass.

Plastic tile is easy to cut with a coping saw or sharp knife of the wallboard type. To cut a piece of tile to fit around a pipe, for example, all you need do is draw or trace the cutout on the surface of the tile, then lay the tile on a wooden cutting surface (a piece of 1 x 10 lumber is fine), and follow the drawn line with the knife or saw. You can make good, smooth cuts this way.

Cutting ceramic tile is more difficult. To make straight cuts—for example, to cut a field tile in half—you place the tile in a tile cutter (which a majority of stores that sell ceramic tile will either loan or rent to you), draw the stylus of the cutter across the tile at the point where you want the cut. You then tap the tile along the line drawn by the stylus, and it breaks cleanly. To finish the cut, you smooth it by sanding the raw edge a little with an emery cloth.

Other cuts—curved, for example—can be made by using an ordinary glass cutter instead of the tile cutter. You can also make some types of cuts with a tile nibbler, which is a type of pliers with cutting edges on its jaws. To use a nibbler, you make a series of tiny nibbles, beginning at one edge, cutting away a small portion of tile with each nibble. You continue cutting until you have formed the cutout shape needed.

If you have a jigsaw, you can also use it to make cutouts in both plastic and ceramic tile. Use a fine-toothed blade of the type used to cut metal for this work. When making such cuts, be sure to wear safety glasses to protect your eyes.

The easiest way to plan a tile job is to make a sketch of the area or areas to be tiled on graph paper. Make the sketch in scale, with four squares of the graph paper representing each square foot on the wall. Find out at your tile store what sizes the tile (and its accessory pieces) comes in. Then, working with these sizes, determine how many field tiles you'll need for the open areas of the wall, and how many accessory pieces, such as bases and caps, you'll need. If you plan carefully, you should be able to compute exactly how many tiles you'll need for the job, right there on the paper.

When you order the tile, it is a good idea to order somewhat more than the plan calls for. For one thing, if you haven't cut tile before, it is

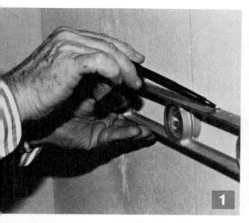 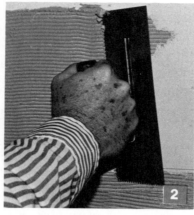 

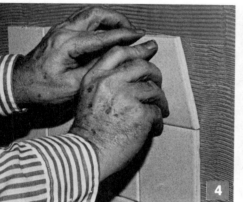 

USE A SPIRIT level to make a horizontal guide line, then apply the tile mastic with a toothed trowel. Press hard on the trowel and spread the mastic thinly and evenly. Position the first tile at the intersection of the vertical and horizontal guide lines, which you should be able to see through the coat of mastic. Apply the second tile next to the first, snapping it into place. Slide it carefully so that it butts against the first tile. Take care to see that the mastic doesn't ooze out between the tiles. Be sure to align the tiles while the mastic is still pliable.

worthwhile to waste a couple of pieces in order to practice cutting. You'll find you become proficient quite quickly—and it helps to know during this practice that it doesn't make any difference if you mess up a couple of cuts.

If you are using the small mosaic tile, you won't have to do much cutting. When you have

to cut a larger tile, you'll find it easiest to do the job on a tile cutter, a jigsaw, or with a coping saw. The nibbler, when used right, does a nice job on small tiles.

It is best to order all of the tile you need at one time. The reason is that the color may vary slightly from batch to batch. By getting it all at

A RENTED TILE CUTTER is used to score a tile for cutting. You also can use a glass cutter.

THE SCORED TILE can be snapped easily by placing it on a pencil and applying pressure.

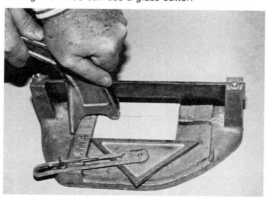 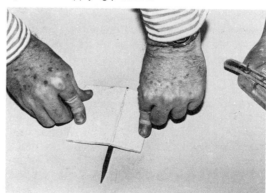

once, you are more likely to get tile in which there is no color variation. Usually you can get a refund on leftover tiles.

Lining up the job

The first thing to remember when you begin to measure the wall for the tile is: no wall is ever true. Even walls which look perfectly square usually are not. For that reason, don't depend on the corner of the wall to provide a perfectly vertical line against which you can align your tiles. Instead, drop a plumb bob with a chalk line from the ceiling, and snap a vertical line on the wall. Use this line as your guide in placing the tiles.

Also, don't assume that the floor or the top of a bathtub is perfectly level. Use a good carpenter's level and draw a horizontal guide line across the vertical line drawn earlier. These two lines, if carefully made, will enable you to set your tile square.

In planning the layout of the tiles on the wall, you'll find that very often the last column of tiles, at the corner or edge of the wall, requires less than a full-width tile. The tile in this last column, for example, may be only 2 in. wide, so you must cut each tile to fit.

For the most professional looking job, however, center the tile pattern so that you don't have a full tile at the left side, for example, and 2-in. tiles at the right. Instead, cut 1 in. from the tiles at the left and 1 in. from the tiles at the right. While this means more cutting for you, it results in a better looking job.

The next step after establishing your horizontal and vertical guide lines is to put the mastic on the wall. Before you open the can of mastic, read the label; then follow the instructions exactly.

You probably will be told to apply the mastic with a toothed applicator and cover 3 or 4 sq. ft. at a time. Then allow the mastic to set for 20 minutes before applying the tile. Do exactly what the label says. You'll get better results.

After the mastic has set the required time, press the first tile in place. Align it carefully with your guidelines, which you should be able to see through the mastic. Begin at the bottom of the area to be tiled, and at one corner. Lay in the entire bottom row, one tile after another.

When placing a tile on the mastic, put the bottom edge into the mastic just touching the tile beneath it and very near the tile to its right. Then sort of "snap" the tile onto the wall. Now press it into its final position, sliding it against its neighbors and seating it firmly in the mastic. Do not slide the tile more than a small fraction of an inch or you may force mastic up between the tiles. However, be certain that each tile is butted firmly against its neighbors, and that the tiles all appear straight and true. You can make adjustments now, while the mastic is still soft.

When all the tiles have been laid, allow the mastic to set according to the instructions. Usually, you are told not to apply the grout for at least 24 hours.

Mix the grout by adding water to make a thick, creamy mixture. Apply this mixture to the spaces between the tiles, using either a small cellulose sponge or a grout float. Work the grout down into the grooves; keep checking as you work to see that there are no unfilled spaces.

As the grout begins to harden, use the rounded end of a toothbrush handle to scrape away excess grout in each groove. The handle provides the proper concave surface to smooth the grout in each groove. After the grout has set hard,

SAND THE EDGES of the cut tile smooth, using emery cloth or abrasive paper.

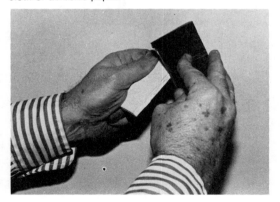

TILE NIBBLERS are used to nibble away bits of the tile until you have cut to the mark.

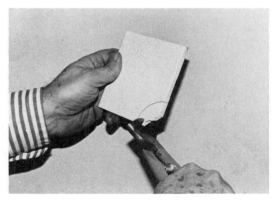

brush the entire wall with a medium-stiff brush to clean away all excess grout. Finally, spray the new grout with a silicone sealer.

In addition to the tiles already described, you can now buy real marble tiles. Made in Italy, these tiles are 6 x 6-in. slabs of genuine marble, ¼-in. thick. They come in several colors and are applied in the same way as ceramic tiles. Decorators use them for window sills, backsplashes for sinks, decoration around fireplaces, fireplace aprons, and as countertops.

Marble may stain or scratch in use, but if it does, you can restore its original beauty by polishing it. You can buy marble cleaners which remove most stains. To apply a new polished surface to scratched marble, buff the marble, using a soft polishing pad in your electric drill. Apply a paste of fine abrasive material first, then polish until the scratches disappear. For an abrasive, you can use an automobile rubbing compound, or a creamy mixture of water and pummice or rottenstone. A fine abrasive provides the brightest polish.

Tile repairs

If you ever have a cracked ceramic tile—which could happen if something heavy falls against the tile sharply—you can remove the broken tile and replace it. To remove a broken tile, use a sharp-pointed tool such as an awl or ice pick to dig out the grout around it. Then insert the tool into the grout's groove and pry upward. The tile should pop off the wall without disturbing its neighbors.

Next, scrape all of the old mastic off the wall. Now apply a thin coat of mastic to the back of a new tile, no more than ¹/₁₆-in. thick. Finally, press the tile in place to make good contact. After the mastic has set for at least 24 hours, apply new grout.

MIX THE GROUT to a creamy paste and apply it to the wall after the mastic has set for at least 24 hours. A rubber-faced grout float is used.

YOU ALSO CAN USE a cellulose sponge instead of a grout float to apply the grout. Be sure to work grout into all of the grooves.

AFTER THE GROUT has set for about 10 minutes, use the rounded end of a toothbrush handle to scrape away any excess in each of the grooves.

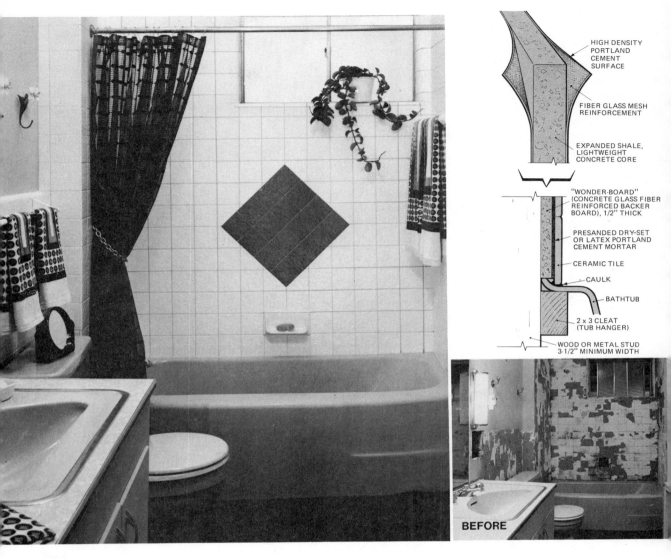

HIGH DENSITY PORTLAND CEMENT SURFACE

FIBER GLASS MESH REINFORCEMENT

EXPANDED SHALE, LIGHTWEIGHT CONCRETE CORE

"WONDER-BOARD" (CONCRETE GLASS FIBER REINFORCED BACKER BOARD), 1/2" THICK

PRESANDED DRY-SET OR LATEX PORTLAND CEMENT MORTAR

CERAMIC TILE

CAULK

BATHTUB

2 x 3 CLEAT (TUB HANGER)

WOOD OR METAL STUD 3-1/2" MINIMUM WIDTH

BEFORE

Ceramic tile for a backup board

■ THE PROBLEM of tiles dropping off walls is common in bathrooms where ceramic tile is installed over gypsum wallboard or gypsum plaster. A new type of backup board can end all those problems, and it's easy to apply.

A panel that's claimed by its maker to be unaffected by moisture, it is made of lightweight concrete reinforced with fiberglass. It won't shrink, swell, delaminate or decay. A 2-in.-wide fiberglass tape that seals joints and corners is also available.

The concrete-fiberglass panels are less than half the weight of the conventional installation of paper, metal lath and Portland cement plaster. They also eliminate the inconvenience of cutting and nailing the paper and metal lath, mixing mortar, troweling on two coats, and the messy cleanup after using wet mortar.

The board is timesaving and easy to use. You can score, snap and nail or screw it to the studs in less time than it takes to apply conventional materials. After the corners and joints are mortared and taped, you're ready to apply tile.

A quality ceramic tile properly installed with

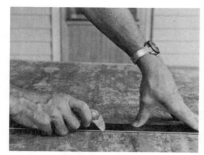

1 Score backup board with a knife. Cut through fiberglass to cement core.

2 After the board has been scored, snap it in two parts along the line.

3 Cut through the bottom fiberglass layer from the other side.

4 Measure the wall to locate needed pipe holes on the board.

5 Using a pencil, mark the pipe holes to be bored in the backup board.

6 Bore or cut holes a bit oversize to permit shifting panel if needed.

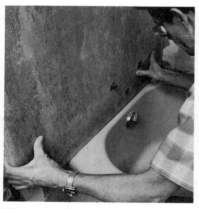

7 Before fastening board to wall, check accuracy of the hole locations.

8 Nail backup board to the studs. Position nails within ½ in. of board edges.

9 Installation is complete. Bottom edge of the board is set on the tub's lip.

10 Next, cut fiberglass tape to lengths needed for all joints and corners.

11 Embed tape in corners and on the seams using a dry-set mortar.

12 Horizontal and vertical joints are mortared, taped and dried.

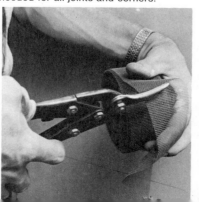

13 Remove pipes. Apply thin layer of presanded dry-set or latex cement.

14 Mark pipe holes on tile. Test-fit by holding tile sheet in position.

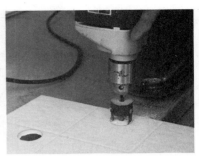

15 Drill pipe holes in tile. This one is Redi-Set pregrouted sheet tile.

16 Install pre-drilled tile on wall and then replace the water pipes.

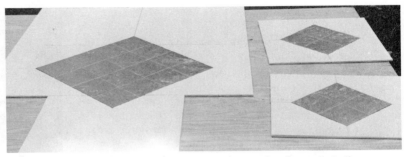

17 For interesting pattern fit tile sheet of contrasting color diagonally to the surrounding sheets. Tile cutter cuts the surrounding sheets to fit.

18 After precut sheets of tile are in place, insert the diamond section.

19 To install soap dish, punch holes in board with a hammer and screwdriver.

20 Apply silicone rubber liberally to backup board and install dish.

21 Grout all joints between sheets with the same silicone used in sheets.

dryset or latex Portland cement mortar over the backup board is an attractive, low-maintenance and long-lasting wall covering for areas subjected to moisture, water and steam.

Boards are available in ½-in. thicknesses in 30x60-in. panels, and 36-in. widths 48, 60 and 72 in. long. The material is also available in a ⅜x36x60-in. panel for installation *only* over plaster, gypsum board, plywood or other equally solid backing. With the thinner ⅜-in. panel you must use fasteners that are long enough to pass through the backing material and anchor firmly in the wall studs. This thinner board is good for remodeling surfaces that present a bonding problem and where space is tight.

Tile the wall behind your stove

■ ENERGY-EFFICIENT, wood-burning stoves are growing in popularity, as are the increasing number of styles and designs offered to meet homeowners' needs. The beauty, safety and efficiency of any stove can be enhanced by surrounding it with ceramic tile. Choosing a combination of stove and tile for your home can be an enjoyable experience. And you'll be surprised to discover how easy it is to install the tile yourself in combination with a glass-mesh, concrete-reinforced shield.

We show how to install the shield and tile on a wall behind a stove, according to UL specifications, which require an air space between the shield and the combustible wall. Installing the floor is an even simpler procedure, since the shield may be laid down directly on the subfloor without provisions for an air space. Check your stove maker's installation instructions for the

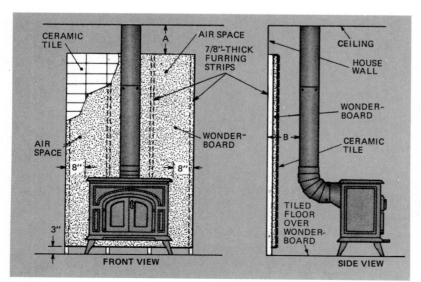

THIS WALL SHIELD provides a 50 percent reduced clearance (as specified by stove maker) from a combustible wall surface. Drawing shows minimum clearances. Clearance (A) may be 1½ to 12 in. for rear-flue-exit stoves, but the shield need not extend higher than 8 in. above the top of a top-flue-exit stove. UL-approved clearance is 3 in. Clearance (B) may vary as specified by stove maker, but it always applies to the flue for rear-flue and to the back of the stove for top-flue-exit stoves. See text for information regarding floors.

minimum area required for floor protection. Then lay the tile on the floor shield, following the same procedure we describe for applying the tile over the wall shield.

You may attach the wall shield to existing plaster or dry wall in any area you choose, but the clearances as shown in the drawing must not be compromised. Study the drawing for minimum clearances for top- and rear-flue stoves.

Note that we show a rear-flue-exit stove in the drawing. Because the rear clearance applies to the flue in this stove design, these stoves require more space, regardless of the use of wall shields. If your primary interest in wall shields is to save space, then you should buy one of the top-flue-exit stoves; or consider replacing your old rear-flue-exit stove.

You can become a pro at working with this backup board in a short time. As it is concrete-reinforced, this kind of shield is heavy (about 4 pounds per sq. ft.) and durable, but easy to cut. Score through the "membrane" on either side

NAIL 2-in.-wide, double-thickness wallshield furring strips to wall, 16 in. on center. Double thickness provides the UL-required ⅞-in. air space between the wall shield and the combustible wall.

FASTEN PANELS with 4-in. nails or dry-wall screws. A double furring strip is needed at all angles, since the shield isn't flexible. Leave a ⅛-in. gap between the panels when you hang them.

APPLY TILE over ⅛ in. of latex-modified portland cement mortar (thin set) mixed with sand. Use spacers for uniformity. To prevent slippage, attach plywood strips to shield bottom with C-clamps.

AFTER PLYWOOD strips are removed from shield bottom, bottom tile course may be set. Apply cement with a square-notch trowel. Use the ¼x⅜-in. notches. Allow wall to cure for two days before grouting.

FILL ALL JOINTS (UL specifications require ⅛-in. spacing between panels) with latex-modified portland cement mortar mixed with sand. Embed glass-fiber tape; cover with more mortar. Trowel the joints flush.

THE COMPLETED wall-shield installation shows a clearance (3 in. from completed floor) between floor and the bottom edge of the shield. Leave at least 1½ in. between the top edge and the ceiling.

APPLY GROUT (various colors available) with a rubber-faced trowel. Work grout in and over spacers, using a diagonal movement. Follow all package directions carefully, as some grouts set very quickly.

with a carbide-tipped scoring tool. Snap the panel along the scored line and then cut the membrane on the other side with one quick run of the tool. You can also use a masonry saw, but this is much more time consuming and produces some dust.

Try not to damage or disturb the surface of the shield in handling, as the adhering quality of cements may be affected. The manufacturer of these shields recommends using a "sanded latex-modified portland cement mortar, applied with a notched trowel to provide a layer of mortar at least ⅛ in. thick over the entire surface to be tiled." The notches in the trowel provide the ⅛-in thickness in patterns of parallel lines. Let the tool

do the work. The mortar will be spread evenly as tiles are pressed into it.

Apply your tile carefully, pushing each tile gently into the mortar and then tapping it lightly to align with adjacent tiles and cross-shaped spacers. This will bring tiles flush with the finished surface.

The photo shows a technique (using C-clamps and plywood strips) for stabilizing the lower courses of tile as you work from bottom up. Don't skip this procedure. Even though the mortar may seem tacky enough to hold the tiles firmly in place, whole areas of tile can slip before you realize it. Thus, this precautionary step is well worth the effort. It's also an easy way to align your first course. By working from the bottom up, you use gravity to help get a good snug fit between tiles.

After the tile is in place, the wall must be allowed to cure for several days before grouting. Whether or not you have experience grouting, make certain you read the manufacturer's instructions to find out the proper working consistency. A little practice will show you that a diagonal stroke is the most effective for working the grout in between the tiles. Continue stroking in a combination diagonal and circular motion until all grout on the surface is distributed in an ever-widening area from the point where you began. Neatness during this step saves effort at cleanup.

After grout starts to set, but before it begins drying to a lighter color, you may want to run over the grout with a finishing tool for a neat finish. Inquire about this procedure and the tool at your tile supplier.

Read a tire

■ TIRES ARE THE ONLY THINGS between your car and the road. For your safety and the safety of your passengers, buy the best you can afford, electronically (spin) balance them and check the pressure and alignment as often as recommended by the manufacturer—or more frequently to be safe.

Parts of a tire

A normal tire has four parts: the tread, sidewall, babrid plies, and the bead that holds the tire secure to the metal rim. The plies give the tire its skeletal structure. The character of the plies determines the tire's strength, stability, and resistance to bruises, fatigue and heat. The plies vary in number and material. *Bias-ply* tires are still used occasionally because of their low cost, but as tire fabricating has advanced technologically, other construction methods have become more popular because they offer better performance. *Radial-ply* tires provide the best combination of wear, handling and overall performance. A radial tire has a body made up of cords that run straight up and over in a hoop fashion from rim edge to rim edge (bead to bead). The tire is reinforced by several tough *belts* of fabric or steel.

Reading a tire

Section 203 of the National Traffic and Motor Vehicle Safety Act passed by Congress in 1966 provided for the establishment of a uniform quality grading system for car tires. The aim was to make it easier for consumers to select the best tires for their driving needs. In 1974, the National Highway Traffic Safety Administration (part of the Department of Transportation—DOT) proposed a set of standards that includes ratings for tread wear, traction, and temperature resistance. These ratings show as molded or printed symbols on the side of the tire.

Learn how to "read" your tire by studying the following illustration and explanation of the markings.

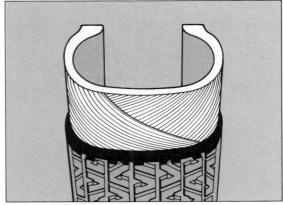

IN BIAS-PLY TIRES, the fabric cords or plies are molded to the carcass of a tire in a crisscrossed pattern. The angle of these cords to each other determines certain characteristics of the tire—high-speed stability, ride harshness and handling.

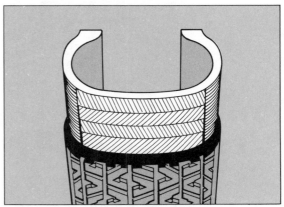

A RADIAL TIRE has a body made up of cords that run straight up and over in hoop fashion from rim edge to rim edge. To provide puncture resistance, long life and tread stability, two or more belts are run around the tire's circumference under the tread.

TREAD DEPTH less than 1/16 inch is illegal in many states. About 11/32 is optimum depth for a new tire. When tread is worn down to 1/16 inch, the tire no longer can provide the traction you need for safety. A penny inserted into a groove in the tread, with the top of Lincoln's head pointing toward the tire, can tell you if the tire is unsafe. If you can see all of Lincoln's head, it's time to replace the tire.

READING A TIRE

BY READING the sidewalls of a tire, you can learn its size, design and construction specifications.

F78-14 (REPLACES 7.75-14). This indicates a current size marking together with its equivalent bias tire-size designation.

LOAD RANGE B. The letter **B** indicates a 4-ply rating. As letters progress in the alphabet, load range increases. For example, **D** would be the same as a former 8-ply rating.

MAX LOAD 1500 LBS @ 32 PSI MAX PRESS. This indicates the tire's load limit and maximum cold inflation pressure. For normal operation, follow pressure recommendations in the owner's manual or on the instruction sticker in the car.

4 PLIES UNDER THREAD (2xxxx CORD) + (2xxxx CORD) SIDEWALL 2 PLIES xxxx CORD. This indicates the tire ply composition which depends on the materials used.

DOT xxxx xx xxxx. The letters **DOT** certify compliance with the Department of Transportation tire-safety standards. Adjacent to this symbol is a tire-identification number. The first two characters identify the tire manufacturer. The remaining characters identify size, type, and date of manufacture. When buying new tires, be sure the seller records your name, address, and tire-identification numbers as required by federal law.

TUBELESS. The tire must be marked either tubeless or tube-type. If a radial tire, the word radial must also be carried.

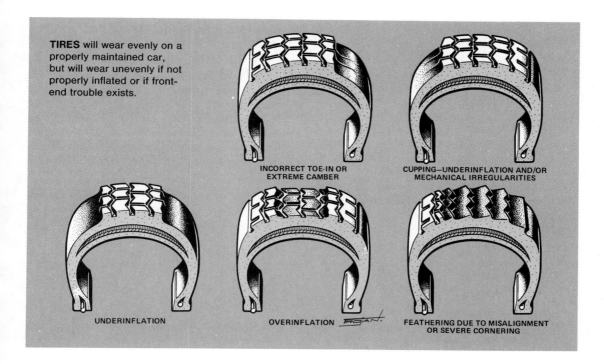

TIRES will wear evenly on a properly maintained car, but will wear unevenly if not properly inflated or if front-end trouble exists.

INCORRECT TOE-IN OR EXTREME CAMBER

CUPPING—UNDERINFLATION AND/OR MECHANICAL IRREGULARITIES

UNDERINFLATION

OVERINFLATION

FEATHERING DUE TO MISALIGNMENT OR SEVERE CORNERING

Tire care

■ DID YOU EVER WONDER why your tires are wearing unevenly? Or why your radials have a tendency to shimmy? Perhaps it has to do with unequal inflation pressure or the pattern you used the last time you rotated them.

Unequal inflation pressure between radial tires will hamper vehicle stability. Keep your pressure gauge handy always. You may actually extend the useful life of radials beyond 40,000 miles, and the useful life of bias-type tires many thousands of miles, by checking pressure every day and making certain it is to the recommended level.

Radial tires will exhibit oscillations resulting in shimmy between 50 and 60 mph if tire-wheel assembly balance is the least bit off. The assemblies should be tested, but keep in mind that balancing radials with static-type balancing equipment will probably *not* improve or eliminate the condition.

In a radial situation, tire-wheel assemblies should be balanced dynamically. The dynamic balancer may be off-the-car or on-the-car equipment. Both types are effective.

Before we explain the difference between static and dynamic balance, this important point must be made:

Many car owners believe that any equipment which tests balance on the car is dynamic equipment. This is not the case. Static equipment consists of both the familiar off-the-car bubble balancer and on-the-car equipment that spins the assembly, but with insufficient force to cause oscillation if it is present.

Static dynamic forces

When a wheel-tire assembly is statically out-of-balance, it means that a heavy spot exists at a single point on the assembly. As the assembly rotates, the heavy spot is forced against the pavement with each revolution. This will create a significant vertical vibration—a bouncing effect.

If a tire and wheel assembly that is out-of-balance statically were balanced in midair on a shaft, the assembly would always revolve and come to rest with the unbalanced portion on the bottom, in dead center.

Static or dynamic imbalance?

If you have a problem deciding whether the condition you feel as you drive is being caused by static or dynamic imbalance, remember that static imbalance creates a vibration at slow speeds. Dynamic imbalance shows up at 50 to 60 mph.

Dynamic imbalance refers to a wheel-tire assembly that has masses which are throwing equalization out of kilter at more than a single point. This creates an oscillating effect—a side-to-side movement. Not only will shimmy result, but if the situation is allowed to continue, the tire may develop flat spots. As the offending assembly oscillates, the tire is scuffed against the pavement.

Let's sum it up with two key points:

1. If you are getting a pronounced vibration in a car that's equipped with radial tires and inflation pressure is correct and equal, have the tire-wheel assemblies balanced with dynamic balancing equipment.

2. If the condition persists after balancing, switch tires front to rear.

Instability on the road

Sometimes a car will be unstable towards one side of the road. It doesn't lead straight and has to be oversteered. This can result in a very strenuous driving situation.

The rigid belts in radials when coupled with natural road crown and crosswinds are the factor. Once correct tire pressure is confirmed and it has been established that the power steering gear valve is centered properly and isn't the cause, there is a definite procedure to follow that should eliminate or at least reduce substantially an over-leading condition. Here it is:

Cross-switch the *front* tire and the wheel assemblies only. The car will now lead either in the opposite direction or in the same direction when it's road-tested. If the car should lead in the *opposite* direction, switch the tires as follows: LF to LR, LR to LF, RF to RR, RR to RF. Now:

1. If the car still leads, cross-switch *front* tire only. Road-test it once more.

2. If the car still leads, replace the right front tire with the spare. Test again.

3. If the car still leads, the left front tire is to blame. Replace it.

If the car leads in the *same* direction, the prob-

FOR LONGER tread life, it is strongly suggested that you rotate your tires following these patterns.

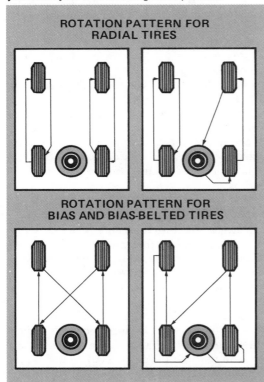

ROTATION PATTERN FOR
RADIAL TIRES

ROTATION PATTERN FOR
BIAS AND BIAS-BELTED TIRES

ACCURATE tire-pressure gauge should always be used to check each tire for proper inflation.

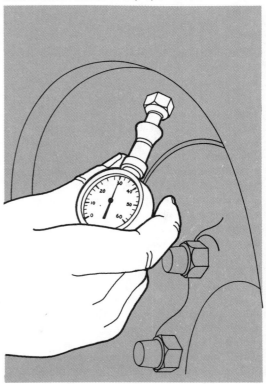

able cause of your trouble is front-end misalignment.

If the car still leads after adjusting the alignment to specification, increase the caster in the direction of lead one-half degree at a time until the pull is eliminated. In other words, if the lead is to the left, increase the left caster—leave the right alone. If the lead is to the right, try increasing the right caster and leave the left one alone.

Additional radial information

Two more facts about radials should be mentioned:

● Never try to eliminate the bulge where the tire contacts the road. It's natural and inflating a radial until the bulge is eliminated will ruin the tire. Inflate to specification only.

● Radial tires can be repaired if they are punctured. However, the puncture must not be more than ¼ inch in diameter, which gives you a lot of latitude, and it has to be confined to the major tread area, between the outer grooves. If the puncture doesn't meet these conditions, the tire should be replaced.

Tire wear tells story

One concern among many car owners is tire-wear patterns. As you can see by the illustrations, abnormal tire wear can usually be traced to one of three things:

1. Underinflation (sometimes it can be overinflation). Having a tire ruined because of this situation is criminal. It only takes a minute a day or a week (or even a month, if the driver is that lazy) to prevent damage.

2. Front-end problems. Tires worn on one side usually indicate excessive camber to that side. If tread edges are feathered, adjust toe-in. Cupped spots are generally the result of tire-wheel assembly imbalanced.

3. Bad driving. Tires that are cracked across the tread or that wear out rather quickly although inflation is maintained often indicate that the driver is engaging in a lot of screeching stops and starts, is trying to negotiate corners and curves on two wheels, and/or is hauling excessively heavy loads. That's only wasting money—new tires don't come cheap.

Out-of-round tires

The only other significant tire problem that we haven't touched on, but one that shows up from time to time, is an out-of-round tire that creates a tramp or thump at 20 to 30 mph. There is a precise procedure you can follow to find the offending tire:

● Inflate all tires to 50 pounds pressure and take the car for a test drive. If tramp has vanished, it confirms the presence of an eccentric tire.

● Now reduce one of the tires to its normal pressure and test drive again. Tramp? If not, then this tire is not the guilty one.

● Continue in this manner, reducing pressure in one tire at a time and test driving, until the reappearance of tramp uncovers the bad tire.

● Return the tire to whomever you bought it from to receive an allowance on a new one.

TREAD-WEAR indicators are built into new tires and are designed to tell you when to replace a tire.

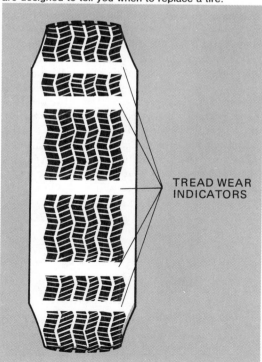

TREAD WEAR INDICATORS

SIDEWALL DAMAGE outside tread area on radials shouldn't be repaired, nor punctures over ¼ in.

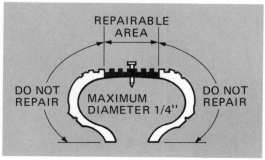

REPAIRABLE AREA

DO NOT REPAIR

MAXIMUM DIAMETER 1/4"

DO NOT REPAIR

Tools

■ TOOLS ARE SO MUCH A PART OF OUR LIVES that it seems almost nothing can be done without them. Projects of almost any magnitude can be done more quickly today if you have a selection of specialized tools available. An understanding of today's basic tools and techniques can give you an appreciation of how things were done in the past.

All tools fall into one of two broad categories: Hand tools and power tools. Because there are so many sub-categories, it is easy for the novice to be confused when considering which tool is required for a given task, or which to add to the craftsman's collection. In an effort to explain away some of the mysteries of tools, we will cover all types and hope to give you a clear understanding of common (and some not so common) tools. Of greater importance, you will get a feeling for those tools that are necessary for your do-it-yourself projects.

• *Tool quality.* Experts have long maintained that there are no worthwhile cheap tools and you get what you pay for. A pair of pliers that sells for a couple of dollars are probably not worth the metal they're made from, and add more in frustration than they save in convenience. On the other hand a quality pair of pliers can be expected to perform well throughout the range of this tool's capabilities and will last a lifetime.

• *Tool safety.* It is an accepted practice in the industry and by expert craftsmen to wear safety glasses when using any power tool and to respect the powered movement of the working part of the tool. Many manufacturers and expert craftsmen alike now recommend wearing safety glasses when using hand tools as well. In almost every case, a pair of safety glasses will protect your eyes from potential serious damage.

> ## ALWAYS
> ## WEAR SAFETY GLASSES
> ## OR GOGGLES to protect your
> eyes when using any power
> or hand tools!

HAND TOOLS

Hand tools, of course, have been around for centuries and with them craftsmen throughout the ages have built a variety of useful and beautiful things—from fine furniture to cathedrals—all without the aid of electricity. While power tools generally will help you accomplish a specific task quicker, you should occasionally remember that almost anything can be done well with hand tools and you will have a better feeling of accomplishment in the bargain.

The large category of hand tools is further broken down into several sub-categories which includes: Cutting, fastening, shaping, hole-making and measuring tools.

CUTTING TOOLS

This category of useful hand tools includes hand saws and knives.

Hand saws

There are several different types of hand saws but the most familiar are probably the crosscut and ripsaw. As their names suggest, the crosscut is for cutting across the grain of a board while the ripsaw is used for cutting with the grain. You should be familiar with the differences between these saws, and be aware of other saws for specialized work.

• *Crosscut saws.* A typical crosscut saw will have from eight to ten teeth per inch of saw blade length. As a rule, the more teeth per inch the finer the finished cut will be. Crosscut teeth on a saw blade are filed at about a 65° angle. This angle lets the teeth shave out wood fibers on the

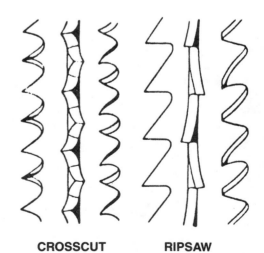

CROSSCUT   **RIPSAW**

downstroke and remove these fibers from the cut on the upstroke.

• *Ripsaws.* Ripsaws are used for cutting with the grain of wood. Because of this, fewer teeth per inch are necessary when compared with the crosscut saw. A typical ripsaw will have about five teeth to the inch of saw blade. In addition, ripsaw teeth differ from crosscut teeth in the angle in which the teeth are filed. As a rule, ripsaw teeth are filed at a 90° angle and this results in a chiseling cut rather than the shaving cut of a crosscut saw.

• *Backsaw.* Backsaws are most commonly mounted on miter boxes and are used for cutting all types of angles in moldings, picture frames and similar projects. Backsaws have many teeth (commonly 11 or more per inch of saw blade) and as a result produce very fine-edged finished cuts. Backsaws, as the name suggests, have a U-shaped piece of steel along the back or top edge of the blade to add rigidity to the blade. In fact, a quality backsaw blade will not flex at all.

• *Miter boxes.* Miter boxes for backsaws are available in a variety of styles and prices. The least expensive are those made from rock maple or plastic and sell for a few dollars. These are useful for making 45° and 90° angle cuts in lumber up to about four inches wide. Much greater accuracy and versatility is possible, of course, with more sophisticated miter boxes. As you can imagine, more advanced miter boxes are more expensive, but still within the reach of most home craftsmen.

• *Coping saws.* Coping saws are not used very much today, having largely been replaced by power saber saws. This is unfortunate because coping saws—primarily used for making shaped cuts in moldings—are more precise than saber saws. The coping saw frame lets it cut far deeper into material than any other saw while at the same time letting you cut an intricate pattern.

For some molding cutting, the coping saw is the only choice.

• *Hacksaws.* Hacksaws are used primarily for cutting metal and no home workshop is complete without a good one. Hacksaws with a tubular back or top are stronger and more long-lived than those simply made from strap steel. A variety of blades are available for hacksaws and it is important to use the right blade for the project. The most common types are 14, 18, 24 and 32 teeth per inch. Hacksaw blades with a large number of teeth per inch are used for cutting sheet metal, steel and hard plastic. Blades with fewer teeth per inch are used for cutting soft metals (such as brass, aluminum and copper) plastics and other metals that would clog finer teeth.

Hacksaw blades are put in the frame so the teeth point forward. A hacksaw cuts on the forward stroke, not on the return stroke. Use two hands for hacksaw work; one on the handle the other on top of the saw, close to the front edge. Don't bear down on the hacksaw when cutting. Instead, *push* the blade through the work. When hacksaw blades get dull, throw them out and replace with a new blade.

• *Keyhole saws.* The last saw worth considering for the home workshop is the keyhole saw. This saw is handy for making a hole in material such as wood, plastic and wallboard. Blades are easily replaced in the pistol grip handle and are available from five to ten teeth per inch. A selection of keyhole saw blades will let you do a variety of hole-cutting tasks.

• *Buying saws.* If you are planning to buy a crosscut saw (or ripsaw) there are several things to keep in mind before you buy. First, look over the saw to see that it is made well—the blade should be finished and embossed with the manufacturer's name; if the saw is taper ground, which is the best type, this will also be embossed on the blade. The overall appearance should be of quality. Next, pick up the saw and hold it at arm's length. The handle should fit your hand well and have at least three screws hold it to the blade. With the saw turned upside down (teeth point up) look along the blade. All of the teeth should be the same eight and evenly sent (alternately left and right).

While the same criterion for choosing a crosscut or ripsaw should be used when shopping for a backsaw, you should also keep in mind that a backsaw is used primarily in a miter box (and often will come with a quality miter box).

The last thing to look for in a quality handsaw is a good general feel or balance. When holding the saw, as if you were going to make a cut, the saw should feel almost like it is an extension of your arm. If it is overly heavy or does not fit your hand well, you'll find it cumbersome to use and your arm will get tired easily. If the handsaw feels balanced and is well made, you can reasonably expect to enjoy using it for a lifetime.

Knives

Another group of cutting tools includes knives and there are several types in this category.

• *Utility knives.* Probably the most familiar and useful is the standard utility knife with replaceable knives. General purpose utility knives come in several styles. Some have retractable blades while others have fixed blades. Some have a long strip type blade, where the front edge can be snapped off when it becomes dull, revealing a new cutting surface.

The variety of blades available for utility knives really makes them useful. There are standard straight blades which can be used for a wide range of cutting tasks. There are also hook blades that make cutting asphalt roofing materials safe and easy. Also hand are long hook blades—called linoleum blades—that are useful for cutting sheet vinyl flooring material. As a rule, almost any cutting task around the home that requires a knife can be easily done with a standard utility knife, outfitted with the right type of blade.

• *Modeler's knife.* For specialty cutting or carving projects you should consider a modeler's knife, such as the kind made by X-Acto. These knives come in a variety of handle shapes—from pencil-shaft types to stout tool handle versions. There are more than a dozen different types of blades for modeler's knives for intricate cuts in all types of materials. There are also shaping blades for carving wooden sculptures. There are even saw blades (similar to keyhole saws) to fit these handles for very small and intricate sawing tasks.

FASTENING TOOLS

Fastening tools are a large category of hand tools that let you join materials of all types. In this category are found screwdrivers, hammers, wrenches and clamps.

Screwdrivers

To the novice or inexperienced worker, screwdrivers may not seem special but, in fact, there are several different types, each designed for a specific purpose. In addition to the standard slotted and Phillips types, there are also Reed and Prince, Pozidrive, Torx, Robertson, and clutch-head screwdrivers.

• *Screwdriver types.* As a rule, most woodworking and some automotive work can be done with standard slotted, Phillips, and Reed and Prince screwdrivers. Most late model automobiles, appliances and mobile homes, however, will usually require one of the specialized screwdrivers—Pozidrive, Torx, Robertson or clutch-head screwdrivers.

• *Screwdriver handles.* In addition to a variety of types, there are a number of different style handles for screwdrivers. Most common, of course, are molded plastic handles but there are also wooden, cushioned and even ball-shaped handles.

• *Purchasing screwdrivers.* Probably the most versatile of all screwdrivers are those with interchangeable tips. These are commonly sold in sets with a screwdriver handle and a variety of different size and shape tips.

Hammers

Hammers are another common hand tool and also a type that bears special consideration. As a rule, different hammers are meant for different jobs, and there is little point in using the wrong hammer.

• *Hammer sizes.* Hammers range in weight from 5-oz. tack hammers to 28-oz. framing hammers. Probably the most popular is the 16-oz. claw hammer, according to industry figures. Unfortunately, the 16-oz. claw hammer is a little too heavy for finish carpentry, such as installing moldings around the floor perimeter and around windows and doors. It is a little too light for extensive framing work. As a rule, a 12-oz. hammer is ideal for finish carpentry and a 20- to 22-oz. hammer is the best choice for framing.

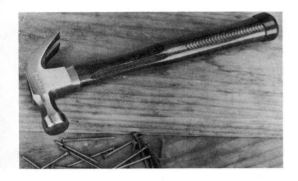

• *Hammer claws.* Curved claw hammers can be used for removing as well as driving nails. Straight claw hammers (also called ripping hammers) are handy for prying off siding or similar materials and are popular with carpenters who specialize in roof conversions and construction framing.

• *Hammer handles.* Handle material for claw hammers includes wood, fiberglass and steel. Generally speaking, steel handles are the strongest, fiberglass is almost as strong and transmits less shock to the hand. Wooden-handled hammers are the weakest but are the most comfortable to use for long periods of time because very little shock is transferred to the hand.

• *Hammer safety.* Hammer safety is an important consideration and should not be overlooked when you are working with this tool. All manufacturers recommend that you wear eye protection when using any striking tool. This is a good habit to get into when hammering.

Wrenches

Another group of tools included in the fastening category are wrenches and there are several useful types.

• *Types of wrenches.* The most common are open end or box wrenches, adjustable wrenches and socket or ratchets. With the exception of adjustable wrenches, all other types are available in either SAE or metric sizes. The well-equipped home workshop should have a selection of both sizes and several different types.

Clamps

The last group of fastening tools included in this section are clamps. These are used mainly for woodworking projects where two or more pieces are to be joined with glue.

It is probably safe to say that there is a clamp for almost any imaginable project. The most common types of clamps include: C-clamps, hand screw clamps, spring clamps, bar or pipe clamps and a variety of special-purpose clamps.

The primary purpose of most clamps is to hold pieces of a woodworking project together firmly while glue sets. When a glue-fastening project is at hand, it is important to choose the right type of clamp. A brief run-down of the uses of clamps may be useful.

• *C-clamps.* C-clamps are used for simple clamping where two pieces are being fastened. A variety of C-clamps are available ¾-in. to over a foot long. Deep C-clamps are also available. These let you clamp material farther in from the edge of the work piece.

• *Hand-screw clamps.* Hand screw clamps are probably the most versatile of all clamps used in woodworking. These wood-jawed clamps have two parallel screws of steel to open and close the jaws of the clamp. They offer the advantage of being adjustable to virtually any angle of clamping needed to get a good grip on the work. These are commonly found with jaw openings from two inches to one foot.

• *Spring clamps.* Spring clamps are small, spring-loaded clamps that resemble alligator clips without teeth. The jaws open wide when the handles are squeezed and clamp tightly when the pressure is released. Spring clamps are very fast and are ideal for clamping small round and flat workpieces.

• *Bar or pipe clamps.* Bar or pipe clamps are used primarily for holding large, flat workpieces together—such as butcher block countertops. Bar and pipe clamps are used extensively in cabinet and furniture-making operations.

• *Web and band clamps.* Web and band clamps are useful for clamping jobs where conventional clamps will not work. The web or band is wrapped around the work and then tightened,

like a tourniquet. These clamps are most useful for gluing chair legs to their stretchers.

• *Corner clamps.* Miter or corner clamps and picture frame clamps are used almost exclusively for holding the four parts of a cabinet or picture frame together while the glue dries. For this purpose they are indispensable.

SHAPING TOOLS

Hand tools that let you shape surfaces are not generally as common in the average home toolbox as the other hand tools. This category includes files and rasps, planes, chisels and gouges. These are all used for woodworking. There are also drywall tools used for finishing interior surfaces that have been covered with gypsum board.

Files

Files are useful to the woodworker not only for smoothing wood but also for shapening all types of tools—from saws to drill bits to chain saws. Generally speaking, files are used for smoothing operations where only a small amount of material must be removed.

• *Flat, round and triangular files.* The most common type of file is the flat file, used to smooth surfaces of almost all types including wood, plastic laminate edges and metal. Flat files are also required for sharpening circular saw blades, axes and similar tools.

Untapered round files are used for sharpening chain saw chains and are generally available in sizes that match common saw-chain tooth sizes—5/32-in., 7/32-in. and 13/64-in.

Tapered and triangular files are commonly used for sharpening handsaws.

• *File care.* Files require a moderate amount of care to remain sharp and serviceable as long as possible. In almost all cases, a file card can be used to restore a file to like-new condition. A file card—which is simply a two-sided brush with steel fibers on one side and stiff bristle fibers on the other—is used to clean the grooves on the file. Unless the teeth have been damaged, a file card will quickly restore the cutting ability of a file.

Rasps

Rasps are similar to files except that their teeth are much coarser.

• *Rasp uses.* Because of the greater tooth size, rasps are used for removing much greater amounts of materials than files. As a rule, a rasp is used in woodworking to shape a surface first and followed by a file then sandpaper. Finer shaping tools must follow the rasp because it leaves the surface rough.

Rasp care is much the same as the care recommended for files, with the file card able to restore much of the cutting ability of a rasp as it does a file.

• *Types of rasps.* A variety of woodworking rasps are available but probably the most useful is the four-in-hand rasp. This specialized rasp has coarse and fine-tooth surfaces, two flat and two rounded.

• *Surform rasps.* The Stanley Tool Company has developed a shaping tool which is really a type of rasp—the Surform line of tools. There are presently eight models of Surform tools. Unlike rasps, a variety of finishes are possible with Surform tools. If a great deal of material is to be removed, the Surform tool is used at a 45° angle to the work. For a well-smoothed work surface, use the Surform parallel to the work surface. If you want to get an almost polished effect on the work surface, use a slightly reverse angle as you move the tool over the work. The one unique feature of Surform tools is that they do not become clogged with material during use as files and rasps do.

Planes

Planes are useful hand tools for smoothing surfaces in woodworking. There are several types, each used for a specific purpose.

• *Types of planes.* Generally speaking, planes are named and sized for the jobs they are intended to do. Bench and block planes are designed for general surface smoothing and squaring. The jack plane is used primarily for smoothing with the grain, along the edge of a board for example. As a rule, the length of the jack plane's sole is around 14 inches, a smooth plane about 9 inches, and the jointer plane will have a sole length of 20 to 24 inches.

• *Block planes.* Block planes are smaller than bench planes and are used primarily for smoothing the end grains of lumber. Block planes are about six inches long and are handy for all types of small planing jobs.

• *Bench planes.* A significant difference between block planes and bench planes is the angle of the blade. On bench planes this angle is around 45°. Block planes, on the other hand, will have a blade angle of about 21° to as little as 12°. The lower the blade angle, the finer the finish.

• *Rabbeting planes.* Rabbeting planes are for general use in close quarters and are ideally suited for cutting rabbet joints. Most rabbet planes come with special guides to aid in making rabbet cuts in lumber.

• *Toothing planes.* Toothing planes are used for roughing up wood surfaces before gluing down veneers or plastic laminates. Toothing planes are about 8 inches long and have small ridges or teeth across the blade. The blade itself is set at a rather sharp, almost upright angle.

• *Circular planes.* A circular plane has a flexible sole and can be used to plane convex or concave surfaces. This is a very specialized plane found in cabinet and furniture making shops.

• *Spokeshaves.* Spokeshaves are best described as a two-handled plane with a very short bottom and wide throat. Primarily, spokeshaves are used for smoothing irregular or curved surfaces. Both straight and curved blades are available.

• *Drawknives.* A drawknife is primarily used to rough shape lumber before planing with a conventional plane. A drawknife has a flat blade with tangs bent down at each end for wooden handles. In use the drawknife is pulled toward the user, angling the blade to control the depth of cut. The drawknife is handy for all types of surfaces but is only used for rough rather than finish planing.

Chisels and gouges

Woodworking chisels are hand and common in the average home workshop and there is a wide selection of quality chisels available.

• *Chisel uses and types.* Chisels are used for a variety of wood removal tasks—from installing a strike plate and hinges in a door jamb to making a mortise and tenon joint in woodworking.

Woodworking chisels range in blade width from ¼ in. to 2 in. A good selection for the do-it-yourselfer would include one each of ¼, ½, ¾ and 1 inch-wide blades. With a set of chisels like this, you should be able to tackle any wood removal project.

• *Chisel handles.* Handle material on modern chisels includes wood and high-impact plastic. For long life, plastic is probably the better choice. Wooden chisel handles, however, are more aesthetically pleasing to use but generally do not last as long as plastic-handled chisels. High quality wooden-handled chisels will have at least one steel ring below the head to prevent splitting.

• *Gouges.* Gouges are a form of chisel. Gouges are used primarily for working on or creating curved surfaces. For most types of rough, curved work a suitable sized gouge is the ideal tool.

Drywall tools

Almost any modern home has interior walls

covered with drywall (also called gypsum board or sheetrock). This wall covering is easy to install and, with a few specialized tools, simple to finish. All that is usually required is a selection of broadknives and corner finishing tools.

• *Using drywall tools.* Understanding how drywall is finished will indicate the proper tools for the task. As a rule, an 8-in. and a 12-in. broadknife are used for finishing flat joints. In addition, corner finishing tools are required for both inside and outside corners.

It is important to remember that professional-looking taped joints are only achieved with the proper tools. Clean tools work best so it is advisable to rinse off broadknives and corner tools often during use.

HOLE MAKING TOOLS

A small selection of hand tools for making holes in material is available for the do-it-yourselfer. The list includes: brace and bit, hand drill, push drill and awl. While almost all of these had tools have been replaced by the electric drill, there remain some hole-making tasks that are best done by hand.

Brace and bit

The brace has been around for about four centuries but it was not until about 1900 that the present adjustable chuck came into existence. A brace is a hand tool that you won't find much use for unless you are making holes larger than ¾ inch or you're working where electricity is not available.

• *Fixed auger bits.* The working end of any brace is the auger bit and these are available in two types and at least thirteen different sizes. The Irwin auger bit has a solid core which many feel is the strongest of all auger bits. The Jennings auger bit design is a spiral that produces a very clean hole and is popular in cabinet and furniture making shops. Jennings auger bits cost about twice as much as Irwin bits.

• *Adjustable auger bits.* One other type of

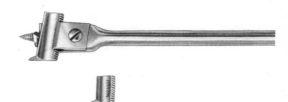

auger bit worth mentioning is the expansive bit. In truth almost all of your boring with a brace and bit can be done with an adjustable expansive bit. There are two sizes available: The first will bore holes for ⅝ to 1¾ in. and the second size bores holes from ⅞ to 3 in. As a rule, holes made with an expansive bit will not be as clean as those made with standard auger bits. Except for cabinet or furniture making, all are within acceptable limits for general woodworking.

Hand drills

The hand drill is a rare tool around the average workshop, having almost totally been replaced by an electric drill. There are some instances, however, where a hand drill is useful—such as drilling screw pilot holes in cabinet making. A hand drill is not as fast as an electric drill and can, therefore, be controlled better. Hand drills use standard twist drill bits and are most useful with the smaller diameter bits.

Push drills

Push drills are very similar to a spiral ratchet screwdriver. These are most useful for drilling small diameter pilot holes in all types of woods and plastic material. As with the hand drill, push drills have almost totally been replaced by the electric drill.

Awls

The awl is quite handy for a variety of tasks. A sharp awl is perfect for marking material to be cut, locating a drill point, widening a hole, starting a hole and for use as an alignment tool for screw holes.

MEASURING TOOLS

An old, time-proven rule of carpentry is, "measure twice, cut once." No matter how ambitious the do-it-yourself project you do, you still need to know precisely the size, volume or shape of many things. There are a number of tools to help you measure including rulers and squares.

Rulers

The do-it-yourselfer must have a good ruler

and know how to use it effectively. In addition, you must be able to transfer measurement accurately and make clean cuts in all types of materials.

• *Steel tapes.* Probably the best all-around choice of a ruler is a steel tape at least 8 feet long. The blade should have a hook on the end and the case housing should have some kind of locking mechanism to keep the blade extended, if necessary, during use. Markings on the blade should be easy to read and be in graduations of 1/16 in. A belt clip on the side of the case will make the ruler handy to carry around and it will always be at your side when you need it.

There is a broad selection of steel tapes available, from 8 to 50 feet long. Professional carpenters seem particularly fond of 25 ft. long, 1 in. wide steel tapes.

• *Folding extension ruler.* A folding extension ruler is another general purpose ruler. These are available in 6 and 8 ft. lengths. A few years ago, folding extension rulers were widely used by professional and amateurs alike. Now, however, extension rulers have been replaced by steel tapes. An extension ruler is still very handy for a variety of projects around the home. A unique feature of the folding ruler is that it is easy to used in confined spaces. The extension feature makes inside measurements simple. All you need to do is fold the rule into one length shorter than the space being measure, then slip out the extension for an accurate inside measurement.

• *Yard sticks.* There are many small measuring tasks in the average home workshop that will not require a long ruler. In fact, many things can be done with a one-piece ruler, one to three feet long. Most useful are those rulers and yard sticks that have both inch and metric scales. Metal yard sticks, that won't break as easily around the shop, are also available.

• *Ruler accuracy.* Accuracy in measuring cannot be overstressed. The best ruler in the world will be of little value if it is read incorrectly. Take the time to earn how to use your ruler correctly and make a habit of double checking your measurements.

Squares

Besides a good folding ruler or steel tape, there are other measuring aids or guides to help you succeed in your building or remodeling projects. Probably the most useful group of these are squares. There are four you should know about: Combination square, carpenters or framing square, try square and T-bevel.

• *Combination square.* The combination square is undoubtedly the most useful measuring aid. These are offered in several forms, some with slotted blades others with grooved blades. Both inch and metric versions are available. Some have cast metal heads while others are made of plastic. Most combination squares have a fairly accurate bubble level that is handy for leveling small items, such as a shelf, where a conventional level would be difficult or impossible to use.

The primary purpose of the combination square—as with all other types of squares—is to let you mark a straight line across a board. This line, of course, is then followed with a saw. In

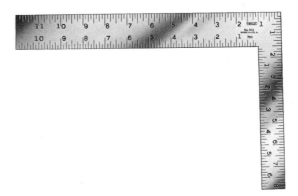

addition to 90° cut lines, all combination squares also make perfect 45° angle lines simply by turning the square over and using the 45° scale.

• *Carpenter's square.* The carpenter's or framing square is another measuring aid widely used in carpentry. It is also very helpful in the do-it-yourselfer's home workshop. Essentially, it is a steel right angle that resembles the letter "L." One side is 24 in. long and the other 16 in. long. The framing square has a number of uses, but, as you might guess, has the most value when framing walls, roofs and ceilings. Special scales and tables are stamped on the blade to indicate the angles to cut rafters. The framing square is also useful when installing wall or floor tile.

• *Sliding T-bevel.* Another important aid in measuring and cutting is the sliding T-bevel. This is the least likely tool to be found in the average home workshop. Sliding T-bevels have a blade that folds out of the handle, much like a pocket knife. A locking screw passes through the handle and can be used to hold the blade in a fixed position. The sliding T-bevel is handy for duplicating angles during home renovations.

ELECTRICAL POWERED TOOLS

Today, almost any task that requires a tool can be done with an electrically powered tool. There are advantages to power tools that are immediately apparent. For example, power tools are faster and more accurate than hand tools used for the same task. A hand-held power circular saw can cut through a piece of 2 x 6 dimensional lumber in seconds; a hand saw may take two minutes to make the same cut. As with hand tools, power tools can be divided into a number of categories including: Cutting tools, fastening tools, shaping tools and hole making tools.

POWER TOOLS THAT CUT

The category of power tools that cut is undoubtedly the largest of all. Generally speaking, there are two types of power tools that cut: portable or hand held, and stationary. As a rule, hand held cutting tools are less expensive, reasonably accurate and faster to use than stationary power tools. Stationary power tools are, of course, capable of making precision cuts and this is their main advantage.

Hand-held power saws

The most common types of hand-held power saws are the circular saw, the sabre saw, reciprocating saw and the chain saw.

• *Circular saws.* The hand-held circular saw is probably the most often used power tool in the building industry and almost as popular with do-it-yourselfers. Hand-held circular saws (often called skillsaws after the inventing company,

Skil) are available in blade sizes from 4½ in. to 10¼ in. The 7¼ in. blade is the most popular.

Besides the blade diameter, another consideration when choosing a hand-held circular saw is the horsepower rating. As a rule, the lower-priced units will have lower horsepower and this will not be a problem unless you use the saw often to cut dimensional lumber (2 x 4, 2 x 6, 2 x 8) where greater horsepower (at least 2 hp) is required.

• *Sabre saws.* According to industry statistics, the most popular type of hand-held power saw is the sabre saw. Part of the reason for this is the low selling price. As a rule, the more you spend on a sabre saw the more features it will have such as greater horsepower, variable speed adjustment, tilting base and rotating head.

The real value of a sabre saw is in making curved or contoured cuts in common building materials such as plywood and up to two-inch-thick lumber. With a variety of blades available, it's easy to understand the popularity of this power tool.

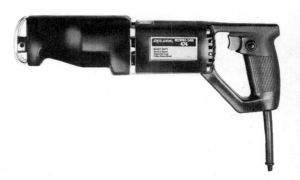

• *Reciprocating saws.* A reciprocating saw is really a heavy duty version of the standard sabre saw. This took is popular with professional carpenters, plumbers and electricians. A variety of heavy duty blades are available for reciprocating saws so it's possible to cut all types of building materials and many metals.

• *Chain saws.* The last type of hand-held power saw to be covered here is the chain saw. There are two types in general use: the gasoline powered and electrically powered. Because there is such a wide difference in price for chain saws, it's best to let your present and future needs dictate the type you require.

It's important to keep in mind that unless you need a chain saw on an almost daily basis, you can probably get along quite well with a lower-priced model—perhaps even renting one. Electrically powered chain saws are usually lower in price than gasoline power units. But, you will always require an extension cord with an electric chain saw, a fact that poses many limitations.

Stationary saws

Stationary saws are necessary for woodworking shop conditions where precision cuts must be made in common building materials. There are four basic types of stationary saws available: table saw, radial-arm saw, band saw and jigsaw.

• *Table saws.* The table saw is probably the most popular stationary saw. A variety of models are available with blade sizes ranging from 8 to 12 inches. Blade height and angle are fully adjustable making the table saw very versatile for even difficult woodworking projects. The table saw is also called a bench saw.

Probably the greatest development in table saws in recent years is the computerized table saw from Sears Roebuck and Company. Basically, the Sears Electronic 10-inch table saw is the same as their standard 10-inch table saw but instead of adjusting blade height or angle with a hand crank, a computerized push button control panel has been added. The panel lets you adjust the blade height or angle by simply punching in the setting you want. For example, if you want the blade height to be 1 in., you simply press the blade height button then 1.00 and the blade adjustment motor raises or lowers the blade to this height. The same procedure is used for adjusting blade angle. Sears claims accuracy of the Elec-

tronic 10-inch saw to be within 0.005 in.

• *Radial-arm saws.* A radial-arm saw is probably the second stationary power saw that serious woodworkers purchase. Many feel this tool is much more versatile than a table saw. Some of the unique features of a radial-arm saw include the ability to accept router bits, rotary surface planes, sanding drums and discs, dado heads, and molding heads. There is usually a second spindle running at a different speed and it can accept flexible shafts to run light grinding wheels.

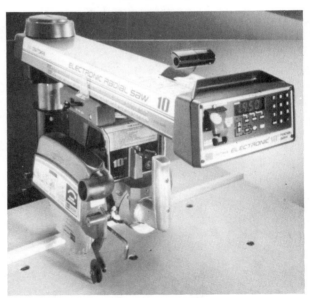

The primary difference between a table and a radial-arm saw is best observed when making a crosscut. On a table saw, you hold the work piece against the miter gauge and move it into the blade to make the cut. On a radial-arm saw, however, you hold the work against a rear fence and pull the blade toward you to make the cut. On a table saw the blade spins upward and toward you. On a radial-arm saw the blade spins down and away from you.

• *Band saws.* The band saw is a specialized stationary cutting tool that will let you make curved cuts in wood stock up to six inches thick. A band saw is indispensable for furniture making, as many pieces are curved or odd shaped—generally an impossible cutting task on a table or radial-arm saw.

Besides cutting, most band saw blades can be replaced with a sanding belt that's ideal for smoothing the intricate shapes you cut with the saw. A variety of band saws blades are available, from ⅛ in. to ½ in. wide making it possible to cut a variety of curves in wood and some metals.

• *Stationary jig saws.* The stationary jig saw is much the same as a hand-held sabre or reciprocating saw except it can cut thicker materials with much greater accuracy. Single and variable speed modes are available with blade speeds ranging from 650 to 3450 strokes per minute (spm).

A stationary jig saw offers many of the advantages of a band saw at a much lower price. Accessory kits with flexible shafts are available to increase the versatility of the jig saw. These kits include a flexible shaft attachment, sanding discs, drum sander, extra blades, grinding wheels and some other components useful with flexible shaft tools.

POWER TOOLS THAT FASTEN

Power tools that fasten include power staplers, power hammers, soldering tools and electric glue guns.

Power staplers

Power staplers are extremely handy for a variety of projects around the home and shop. They make short work of reupholstering furniture, putting up plastic sheathing around windows (as a quick alternative to storm windows), installing insulation between wall studs and joists, and for assembling some plywood projects (such as ¼-in.-thick plywood backing for cabinets). Most electric staplers will accept a wide range of staples from ¼ in. to ⁹⁄₁₆ in. long.

Brad nailer

Another handy fastening tool is the electric brad nailer. This tool is similar to the electric stapler except it has the ability to drive wire brads into common building materials such as moldings, particleboard and some hardwoods. Standard lengths of brads are 1 in. and 1¼ in. long in white or dark colors.

Power nailers

Power nailers, often called power-actuated hammers, are the best tool for driving nails into concrete. In use a power charge (similar to a .22 caliber blank cartridge) is used to drive a special nail. When the head of the tool is struck with a hammer it sets off the charge, forcing the nail into the material with great force.

More than the usual care must be taken when using power nailers, and safety goggles are an absolute must.

Power nailers have been around for many years but their cost was prohibitive except for professionals. Single shot units are now available at a relatively low cost. These do much the same thing as power hammers selling for ten times as

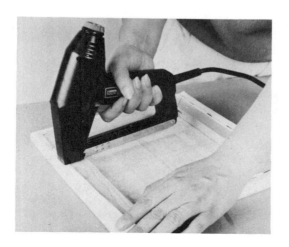

much. A variety of charges and nail lengths are available for fastening a wide range of materials.

Soldering tools

Electric soldering tools are necessary for repairs to electronic equipment around the house. Probably the best all-around choice for the do-it-yourselfer is an electric soldering gun. Kits are available with a gun and a selection of tip sizes for almost any soldering project. For fine soldering work, however, such as printed circuit board repair or building, the pencil type soldering iron is a much better choice.

Glue guns

Electric glue guns offer the capability of making almost instant repairs to a wide range of materials. Part of the beauty of hot glue is that it sets up as quickly as it cools, in most cases this is around 20 seconds. The use of hot glue eliminates the need for clamps or waiting so it's handy for quick repairs around the house. Special caulking can also be applied with some glue guns.

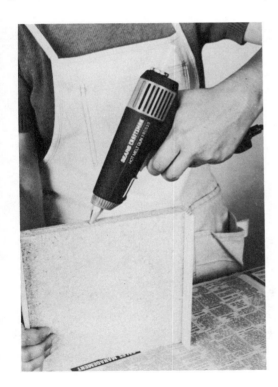

POWER TOOLS THAT SHAPE

Power tools that shape include routers, sanders, lathes and jointer-planers. They are classified as either hand-held or stationary.

Hand-held shaping tools

Shaping tools that you can hold and work in your hands include routers and sanders.

• *Routers.* The hand-held router is a popular tool among serious woodworkers. With any of the special bits installed, you can quickly accomplish a variety of tasks that would take hours—in some cases days—with hand tools. The capabilities of a router include decorative edging and detailing, making dovetail joints, cutting dados, grooves and rabbets. A router is also the best tool for trimming plastic laminate material on countertops.

Routers are available in several sizes ranging from single hand units, handy for trimming plastic laminate, to large two-handed models suitable for edging hardwoods. There are also accessories available so you can use your router as a lathe or wood figure duplicator.

• *Power sanders.* Power sanders are useful for finishing projects around the house and they are either hand-held or stationary.

There are two basic types of hand-held units: belt sanders and pad sanders. Belt sanders remove material quickly and are useful for large sanding projects. Pad sanders, often called finish sanders, remove material slowly and are, as the name suggests, used for finishing off a surface before a coating of paint or varnish.

Stationary shaping tools

Some sanders are stationary shaping tools as are lathes, jointers, and planers.

• *Stationary sanders.* Stationary sanding machines are for the more serious woodworking shop. Almost all types have the capability of belt and disc sanding. While professional disc/belt sanders are a worthwhile investment, the do-it-

yourself woodworker will find a much more reasonable price on any of the mini or compact units hobbyists use.

• *Lathes.* The woodworking lathe is a specialized tool not found in the casual shop. With a lathe it is possible to create table and chair legs, railing stiles, wooden bowls and other turnings. Besides the lathe itself, wood turning also requires a selection of special lathe chisels.

• *Jointer/planers.* Jointer/planers are another specialized woodworking tool popular with professional and serious woodworkers. This machine is used to chamfer edges on lumber and is also required when making furniture where the joint edges must have a tight, flush fit. The jointer/planer is also used for planing rough surfaces and squaring edges, up to six inches wide on some units.

POWER TOOLS THAT MAKE HOLES

Electric drills come in both hand-held and stationary models.

Portable electric drills

Electric drills are common and can be found in almost any toolbox in America. Some of the features on the more expensive models include variable speed, ⅜-in. or ½-in. chucks, reversible direction and speed control.

Growing in popularity among both professionals and do-it-yourselfers are cordless electric drills. Some of the attractive features of cordless drills include the ability to use the drill without an extension cord, variable speed, reverse, removable battery packs, and two gear ranges.

Drill presses

For precise drilling, drill presses are available. These stationary units let you bore holes in almost any type of material from wood to metal. Unfortunately, stationary drill presses are expensive, so they are generally limited to professionals.

Many of the hobbyists drills have accessory drill press stands, extending the versatility of these small power tools. Much less costly are the portable drill press stands used with a standard electric drill. While not as precise as standard drill presses, drill stands offer generally acceptable accuracy for most do-it-yourself projects.

MORE ABOUT TOOLS

As you have seen in this introduction, there are many different tools available. Some are handy for home projects while others are in the realm of the professional. In the pages that follow you'll gain solid information about how to get the most out of many of these tools and, in the end, make you a better craftsman.

Tool selection and use

■ STUDYING AND COMPARING TOOL SPECIFICATIONS can influence your tool-buying decisions. At one time, a portable power tool was fairly simple. You'd go to the local lumberyard or hardware store and buy a tool with a brand name you trusted. It was often the same tool your father used. Purchases were based mostly on personal preference and past experiences. Although these are still two valid reasons for purchasing a tool, they alone are not enough.

The tool market

Today, manufacturers are offering more tools than ever before, and it's important to study the details, the specifications, before buying. The introduction of foreign tools has created a competitive market similar to the situation found in the automobile industry—quality products available in a wide range of prices.

Today's toolmakers recognize the need for a wide range of products to satisfy all skill levels. It wasn't long ago that the homeowner had only two choices: Pay top dollar for a high-quality, professional-grade tool or buy a light-duty, low-quality tool. There were no middle-range tools for the average do-it-yourselfer. Now, manufacturers commonly produce a consumer, tradesman and professional line of tools.

Tools are also available at more places than ever before. Besides the lumberyard and hardware store, power tools are sold at home centers, discount department stores, mass merchandisers, manufacturer's service centers and through mail-order tool companies. So it's easier to buy the tool that is just right for your budget and skill level. But deciding on a specific model is more difficult because of the many choices available. For example, Skil makes 14 different circular saws and Black & Decker offers more than 50 drill models. The first step in making an intelligent buying decision is so research the tool market so you can compare and evaluate the tool specifications of different brand tools. By doing this, you'll learn which ones are best suited to your purposes.

Do your homework

All major toolmakers offer a catalog that describes each tool in detail. Studying the catalogs is a great way to compare the specifications—amps, horsepower, weight, capacities, bearings, rpm—of one tool to another. Tool specifications can be clues to the expected performance of a hand tool and can justify the price difference between two seemingly identical tools. Tool catalogs also provide valuable information about warranties, accessories, service center locations and tool operator safety. When ordering a catalog, be sure you ask for a current retail price schedule, too.

After studying the catalogs, bring them to the stores for use as reference guides. You'll find that most stores carry only a few models of each tool from two or three manufacturers. Contact the manufacturer if you're having trouble locating a specific tool and ask for a list of tool dealers in your area.

Another important factor to consider before purchasing a power tool is the location of the nearest authorized service center. If the tool breaks down, you shouldn't have to send it back to the manufacturer for repairs. Check the tool catalog for the nearest service center. Call them and ask a technician about the speed of repairs and the availability of replacement parts. At least one manufacturer, for example, pledges to have a disabled tool operating within 72 hours or they'll provide a loaner tool.

Locating tool specifications

There are four places to find tool specifications: in the tool catalogs, on the tool's packaging, in the owner's manual and on the nameplate affixed to the tool. The catalogs contain the most helpful information regarding tool specifications.

The specifications that will influence your buying decisions the most include the ampere rating (amps), horsepower, what type of bearings are used and if the tool carries an Underwriters' Laboratories (UL) label.

Amp rating. Amps are the standard unit for measuring the strength of an electric current. The amp rating of a tool is usually found on its nameplate.

It's commonly thought that higher amp ratings mean more power, and in most cases this is true. But don't use amp rating as the single deciding factor when comparing tools. A low-grade tool often requires more current to perform the same job as a high-quality, highly efficient tool. The lower-grade tool, therefore, may have a higher amp rating.

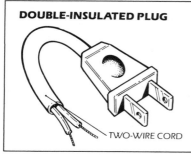

DOUBLE-INSULATED PLUG

TWO-WIRE CORD

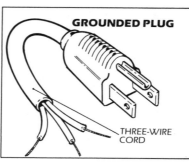

GROUNDED PLUG

THREE-WIRE CORD

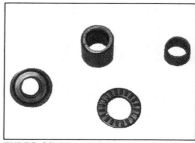

TYPES OF BEARINGS in power tools are (left to right); ball, roller, needle and sleeve.

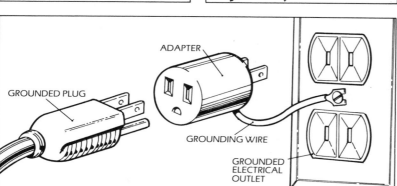

ADAPTER

GROUNDED PLUG

GROUNDING WIRE

GROUNDED ELECTRICAL OUTLET

TOOLS HAVE a double-insulated, two-wire (top, left) or a three-prong grounded plug (top, right). Use an adapter (lower) to match a grounded plug with a two-wire outlet.

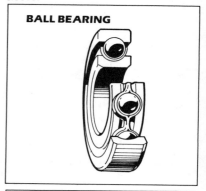

BALL BEARING

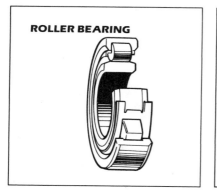

ROLLER BEARING

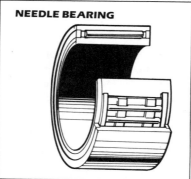

NEEDLE BEARING

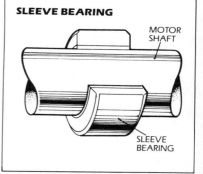

SLEEVE BEARING

MOTOR SHAFT

SLEEVE BEARING

DRAWINGS SHOW CUTAWAY VIEWS of four bearings. The rolling elements, balls, rollers and needles, are held in position by the cage. Sleeve bearings have no rolling elements.

Horsepower. The horsepower rating of a tool motor represents the maximum horsepower the tool can develop, rather than the actual horsepower output when operating at the specified amp rating. In actuality, motors can run for only a very short time at maximum horsepower without burning out. But the horsepower rating does give you an idea of the motor output when comparing tools.

Horsepower ratings are most important when buying a router or circular saw. Choose the horsepower rating depending on the job you're doing. Don't expect a ⅝-hp router to perform the heavy-duty operations of a 2- or 3-hp router. When you're looking for power, look for more horsepower.

Bearings. Discovering what kinds of bearings are used in a tool is probably your most important quality consideration. It's a simple fact that high-quality bearings improve performance and the life of the tool. The types of bearings used are usually listed in the manufacturer's catalog or in the owner's manual.

There are basically four types of bearings used in tool construction (see drawing): ball, roller, needle and sleeve. Occasionally, you'll see ball-thrust bearings, a special type of ball bearing that is designed to resist loads acting in an axial direction to the armature shaft. They're commonly used in hammer drills. Sometimes, a combination of bearings is used, such as ball and roller or ball and sleeve. All ball-bearing construction is considered the most desirable, with ball and roller construction a close second.

Ball bearings consist of steel balls that move within an enclosed circular channel called a cage. Roller bearings, on the other hand, are made of cylindrical rolling elements. Needle bearings are similar to roller bearings except that the rolling elements are longer and generally have smaller diameters. Their one advantage over roller bearings is that they require less space. In every other respect, though, needle bearings perform with far less efficiency than either ball or roller bearings.

A sleeve bearing has no true rolling element and is the least efficient bearing. Sleeve bearings are commonly used, though, in combination with ball and/or roller bearings in quality tools. They're used in areas where the least amount of load will be exerted on the bearing.

Single-sleeve bearings (see photo) are made from powdered bronze or iron impregnated with lubricant at extremely high temperatures. As the sleeve heats up during tool use, the lubricant is released from the metal. Single-sleeve bearings are commonly used in drills.

As you compare tool specifications, you'll find the bearings are often the difference between the regular-duty tool and a heavy-duty model.

Underwriters' Laboratories. While most tool specifications affect a tool's performance and durability, the most important specification, the UL label, assures tool operator safety. The UL label means the tool has been tested and met stringent electrical and mechanical safety standards. Look for the UL label on the tool nameplate, packaging and owner's manual. All major toolmakers carry the UL listing, and we strongly recommend buying only UL-listed tools.

Also, make certain the tool is either double-insulated or has a three-prong grounded plug (see drawing). Both provide protection from the danger of electrical shock.

All power tools have a basic or functional insulation system to separate the current-carrying parts from each other and from the metallic motor components. Without this functional insulation, the tool would not operate. In double-insulated tools, an extra insulating system is provided for additional protection against electrical shock in case the functional insulation fails. Double-insulated tools have a two-wire cord with a two-prong plug.

Grounded tools have three-wire cords and a plug with three prongs, one of which is the ground. A wire connects the ground prong to the tool's metal housing.

Caution: Use a grounded plug only in a matching outlet. Never break off the grounding prong for use in a two-wire outlet. An adapter, as shown, can be used with a two-wire outlet, but *only* if the outlet itself is grounded and the adapter pigtail is attached to the facing plate mounting screw as shown in the drawing. If necessary, you should have an electrician check the electrical outlet for ground.

Double-insulated and grounded tools are equally safe when they are used properly. The average homeowner will find double-insulated tools are more versatile since many homes have two-wire outlets.

Drills

The portable electric drill is by far the most popular consumer power tool. It's available in a variety of styles, capacities, power ratings and prices.

Drills are sized according to the maximum diameter bit accepted by the chuck. The most common sizes are ¼, ⅜ and ½ in. Active homeowners will find a ⅜-in. drill provides a nice combination of power and versatility in a medium price range. Drills are rated by amps and by the no-load speed (rpm). Amps generally range from 2 to 6. The higher the amp rating, the more powerful the drill. The rpm, on the other hand, drop as the power increases. So, if you're looking for power in a drill, buy lower rpm and higher amps.

Two popular drill features are variable-speed trigger control and a reversible motor. Variable-speed allows you to control the bit speed with finger pressure, and the reversing mode is necessary for removing screws and jammed drill bits.

Next, handle the drill. It should feel balanced and comfortable in your hand. Some models have center-mounted handles to distribute the weight evenly, making the tool less nose-heavy. Also, check to be sure the drill manufacturer offers a full line of accessories.

Circular saws

When fitted with the appropriate blade, the portable, powerful circular saw will cut wood, metal, plastics and masonry materials. Circular saws are classified by the diameter saw blade they use. Common sizes range from 4½ to 10¼ in. The 4½-in. saw is a specialty tool used for cutting plywoods, paneling and trim stock. The 10¼-in. saw is an industrial heavyweight that has no practical use for the homeowner. The middle-range models, 7¼- and 8¼-in., better suit the consumer.

The principal difference between these two is that the larger saw has a greater depth-of-cut.

When comparing saws, the tool specifications that influence your buying decision the most include horsepower, amp rating, bearings and maximum depth-of-cut at 90° and 45°.

The safety features to look for when buying a circular saw are an electric brake that stops the blade within seconds of releasing the trigger, and a slip-clutch that prevents dangerous kickback and motor burnout. Should the blade bind in a cut, the clutch will override the connection between the blade and the motor. This allows the motor armature to rotate even though the blade is stopped.

Also, check the saw's retractable blade guard. See that it slides up smoothly, closes quickly when released and operates without excessive play that could cause the guard to hang up. Choose a saw that has a front handle or knob for additional control and a heavy-gauge, sturdy wraparound shoe.

Most circular saws are rated standard-, heavy- or super-duty based on the amps, horsepower and bearings. The best buy would be a standard-duty, 7¼-in., 1½- to 2-hp. 10-amp ball-bearing circular saw.

Sabre saws

The lightweight, portable sabre saw, or jigsaw, is unsurpassed for cutting curves in a variety of materials including softwood and hardwood, plywood, metal, plastic, leather and rubber.

Sabre saws are rated according to horsepower, blade speed and blade stroke length. Consumer saws range from ⅙ to ⅝ hp. As with other tools, more horsepower means greater cutting power. A ⅓-hp sabre saw is adequate for the average do-it-yourselfer.

Saw blade speed is measured in strokes per minute (spm). Saws are available in single-speed, two-speed and variable-speed models. The variable-speed model offers greater versatility and control.

The blade stroke length is the distance that the blade travels in one stroke. A 1-in. stroke length is the most common. Some sabre saws have a scrolling mechanism that allows the blade to pivot 360°. Scrolling sabre saws are worth the additional cost if you need to do intricate, highly detailed scrollwork.

Other points to look for when comparing sabre saws include the cutting capacities in wood and metal and if the shoe is adjustable for cutting angles. Also, examine the saw blade clamp, the fixture that holds the blade in the saw. This is a common weak link in sabre saws. Be sure the blade clamp fits on the saw shaft without excessive play. Any wobbling in this clamp will be transferred to the blade. Be certain the clamp accepts universal, straight shank saw blades. Avoid a saw that uses only specially shaped blades. And finally, choose a saw in which adjustments and blade changes are made with a screwdriver, not a hex-key wrench. It seems you can always find a screwdriver.

Belt sanders

A portable belt sander is a quick, easy way to smooth rough boards and remove old finishes. Sanders are identified according to their belt size and belt speed.

The most popular size sanders are 3 x 21 in., 3 x 14 in. and 4 x 24 in. The 3 x 21-in. sander is a good, all-purpose tool for the home workshop. For light-duty sanding, Skil and Black & Decker each makes a small, easy-to-handle 2½ x 16-in. sander. The power of a belt sander is determined by the amp rating and horsepower. But generally, the larger the belt size, the more powerful the sander.

The belt speed is rated as surface feet per minute (sfpm). Look for this information in the tool catalogs. The best-performing 3 x 21-in. belt sanders operate with a belt speed between 1000 and 1300 sfpm. Be sure the sander has an adjustment knob for keeping the belt on track. Some Skil sanders have an automatic tracking system that eliminates the adjustment knob.

Next, check the belt-changing procedure. The simple practice of changing sanding belts shouldn't be a troublesome task. Choose a sander with a belt release lever for quick belt changes.

Routers

Routers are rated by rpm, horsepower and amps. They're sized according to the maximum diameter bit accepted by the collet (chuck). A ¼-in.-capacity collet is the best choice for do-it-yourselfers. Rpm range from about 15,000 to 30,000. As with a drill, the lower the rpm, the more powerful the tool. Horsepower ranges from a ⅝-hp light-duty laminate trimmer up to a 3½-hp professional router. The mid-range 1- and 1½-hp routers will provide enough power to handle most woodworking operations.

Next, check the router handles for comfort and the on-off switch for convenient location. The trigger switch is the safest because you can squeeze it while keeping both hands on the tool. Toggle and slide switches can seldom be reached from the handles.

Bucksaw you can build

■ IT'S A SAFE BET that your grandfather cut a great many cords of firewood with an American bucksaw. In all likelihood, your dad did too. Now you can make a bucksaw and enjoy using it as well.

Handy for cutting up to 8-in. logs, our version is made of cherry, but any hardwood will do. You don't need a great deal of this expensive wood; a piece measuring 1 x 6⅝ x 25 in. will do.

To begin construction, lay out the three pieces on the hardwood. Cut out the crosspiece first using a bandsaw or sabre saw. Make certain the two handle pieces are cut on the table saw, because you will need square edges for mortising

and to make the blade-holding kerfs.

Cut the handles on the table saw and then lay out the mortises, saw kerfs and holes to be bored. The blade-holding kerf on the long handle is the blade's width by 1⁷⁄₁₆ in. deep. To make the end kerf on the short handle, use either the tenoning attachment for your saw or rig a setup, with clamps, to straddle the fence.

Bore the holes for the blade screws and for the rod at the handle ends. Shape all edges with a rounding-over bit and router, except for that portion of the edges around the mortises.

MAKE THE CUTS for the tenon with crosspiece against the miter-gauge (left). To make blade-holding kerf, clamp the stock and slowly elevate blade to 1⁷⁄₁₆ in.

IN HANDLES, bore overlapping ⅜-in. holes within the outline. Square with a chisel.

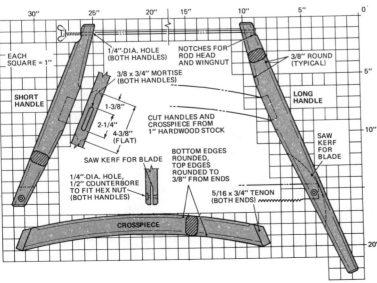

EACH SQUARE = 1"

SHORT HANDLE

1/4"-DIA. HOLE (BOTH HANDLES)

3/8 x 3/4" MORTISE (BOTH HANDLES)

1-3/8"
2-1/4"
4-3/8" (FLAT)

SAW KERF FOR BLADE

1/4"-DIA. HOLE, 1/2" COUNTERBORE TO FIT HEX NUT (BOTH HANDLES)

NOTCHES FOR ROD HEAD AND WINGNUT

CUT HANDLES AND CROSSPIECE FROM 1" HARDWOOD STOCK

BOTTOM EDGES ROUNDED, TOP EDGES ROUNDED TO 3/8" FROM ENDS

5/16 x 3/4" TENON (BOTH ENDS)

3/8" ROUND (TYPICAL)

LONG HANDLE

SAW KERF FOR BLADE

CROSSPIECE

COUNTERBORE nut hole; chisel to hex shape. Tap the nut in with a hammer.

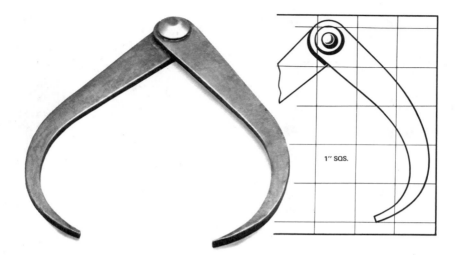

1" SQS.

Fine tools you can make

■ THERE ARE ANY NUMBER of hand tools and fixtures you can make for little or nothing. The eight shown here will prove extra handy at your drill press, lathe and bench. Among them is a fixture called a bench hook that hooks over a bench to hold small work for sawing, filing and the like. Shown in its simplest form, it can be made without much trouble and with a few boards you probably have around the shop.

Another simple item to make is a V-block which is used to cradle and hold dowels and other turnings when the job calls for drilling a hole through a piece dead-center. You will find it to be very valuable and there should be one near any drill press. Old worn-out bastard mill files make great scraping tools for woodturning when bevel-ground and fitted with a long handle. And you can't beat a pair of friction-type calipers for fast adjusting. It's a tool you can make from a couple of pieces of flat metal and a rivet. These are just some of the homemade tools suggested on these pages.

Friction-fit calipers are fast-adjusting

If you have a wood lathe and haven't bought a pair of calipers, don't. You can make a dandy 6-in. pair of friction calipers for far less than you can buy them. They're fast adjusting, for you simply pull them open or squeeze them shut. The legs are held with a roundhead rivet and spring washer. Make a pattern following the drawing above on blue ³⁄₃₂-in. Starret ground flat stock. Scribe the outline on it and cut out with a metal-cutting blade. Finish the sharp edges with a file. Be sure to use a spring washer under the rivet to provide the necessary friction fit.

Lathe chisels from old files

You can make a scraping tool for your lathe from an old file. If the file is long, shorten it to about 10 in. Grind it smooth at the tip, then grind a 60° bevel. Hone the bevel but don't remove the wire edging—it helps the scraping action. Fit it with an 11-in. hardwood handle.

Two-faced sander

With ¼-in. cork glued to one side and ³⁄₁₆-in. leather to the other, this sanding block keeps sandpaper from clogging and glazing. A 1 x 1½ x 5½-in. wood block fits the hand nicely and is the right size to take a quarter sheet of sandpaper. Use white glue to attach the leather and cork facings. Your hand holds the paper in place when you grip the block for sanding.

Handy bench hook

For hand work at the bench you can't beat a bench hook for holding work and protecting the bench's top. Generally it is used with a backsaw but you won't be using it just to saw—you'll be filing on it, chiseling and the like. It's nothing more than a flat board with cleats attached to opposite sides and ends so you can flip it over and use both sides. It's easy to replace.

Save that broken sledge handle

When you're swinging a sledge and wind up with a handle in your hand and no sledge, don't toss it away. The broken handle from a sledge, ax or ball bat provides the best kind of hardwood (hickory and ash) for turning new handles for files and beat-up chisels. The handle for a socket chisel is a simple tapered turning, and when fitting a handle to a chisel with a tang, you can size the collar for a drive-fit ferrule cut from thinwall conduit or brass tubing. For the final step, apply a 50/50 solution of shellac and linseed oil to the wood.

DUST GROOVE

Shooting board produces square edges

A shooting board is a handy gadget for squaring the edge of a board when you don't have a jointer. The plane is used on its side and is pushed back and forth along a wood fence. The work is placed against a stop and on top of the fence. The plane removes the stock overhanging the fence. Tapered stop fits tapered dado and wedges in place. Lower edge chamfer forms dust groove.

Your drill press should have a V-block

V-blocks are needed at the drill press to hold round stock securely and facilitate drilling through the exact center. To make one, cut a 1 x 2 x 6-in. hardwood block and run it through your table saw with the blade tilted 45°. Then run it a second time to form a V-groove. If you lack a table saw, you can mark the V and cut it by hand with a backsaw. Finish the shellac and bore a hole in it to hang by your drill press.

Scratch stock forms bead by scratching surface

When you want to form a small bead along the edge of a table leg or apron, you can do it with a homemade tool called a scratch stock. It's made to fit over the edge of the work and cuts by scraping. All it consists of are two pieces of wood with a blade clamped between. The blade is made from a short piece of hacksaw blade ground to the shape you want. The photo shows the blade pulled out so you can see it. In use, only the tip is exposed in the very corner of the U-shaped block. It makes the neatest beading you ever saw.

Homemade tools you'll be proud of

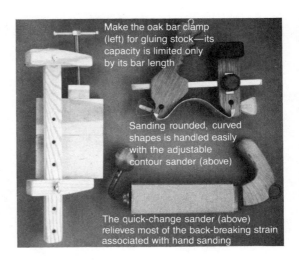

Make the oak bar clamp (left) for gluing stock—its capacity is limited only by its bar length

Sanding rounded, curved shapes is handled easily with the adjustable contour sander (above)

The quick-change sander (above) relieves most of the back-breaking strain associated with hand sanding

■ THERE'S A GREAT FEELING OF PRIDE and accomplishment that comes from creating a project with your own hands. You can take that special feeling one step farther by making the tools shown here to use in creating that project.

The tools are a deep-cut hacksaw, an adjustable contour sander, a quick-change full-sheet sander and an oak bar clamp. Not only are these tools functional, they're handsome as well. The unique combination of rich wood grains with shiny brass and steel makes for a tool that you'll be proud to use and show off. Also, the tools are a bargain, since they're made mostly from shop scraps.

Deep-cut hacksaw

It's no secret that a hacksaw is essential in any shop. But standard hacksaws share a common shortcoming: depth-of-cut is limited usually to less than 4 in. Make the deep-cut hacksaw shown here to complement your standard model saw. With an 8½-in. depth-of-cut, it tackles jobs other hacksaws can't.

First, cut the three saw frame members (parts **A, B** and **C**) from 1-in.-thick oak. Next, cut a ⅜-in.-wide x 2-in.-deep open mortise through the handle (**A**) and a mating tenon in the top frame (**B**). Also bore and notch the bottom of both the handle and front frame (**C**) to accept the angle-irons and steel plates (**K, L, M, N**), and the threaded rods (**H1, I1**) of blade holders. Join handle to top frame using carpenter's glue and two ¾-in.-dia. hardwood dowel plugs.

Attach the two steel pivot bars (**G**) and the two brass bars (**F**) as shown. The bars extend into the frame about ¼ in. to form a channel for the tension bar hexnut (**D**) and the maple pressure block (**E**). Attach the angle-irons and steel plates to form a shaft for the blade holders (**H, I**). Drill and tap each blade holder to accept threaded rods (**H1, I1**). Notch holders and drill ⅛-in.-dia. holes for the steel roll pins (**J**) which hold the blade in place.

CUTTING ENTIRELY THROUGH this 4-in.-dia. PVC pipe would be an impossible task for a standard hacksaw, but not for our deep-cut version.

MATERIALS LIST—DEEP-CUT HACKSAW

Key	No.	Size and description (use)
A	1	1 x 5 x 11¾" oak (handle)
B	1	1 x 3⅝ x 19" oak (top frame)
C	1	1 x 1½ x 9¾" oak (front frame)
D	1	⅝"-dia. x 11¾" steel rod, two hexnuts, one washer (tension bar)
E	1	1 x 1 x 2" maple (pressure block)
F	2	⅛ x 1 x 8¼" brass bar
F1	6	¾" No. 8 fh brass screw
G	2	³⁄₁₆ x ¾ x 11½" steel (pivot bar)
G1	10	¾" No. 8 fh screw
H	1	⅝ x ⅝ x 3" steel (blade holder)
H1	1	⅜"-dia. x 3" threaded rod, washer, wingnut
I	1	⅝ x ⅝ x 1¾" steel (blade holder)
I1	1	⅜"-dia. x 3" threaded rod with washer and wingnut
J	2	⅛"-dia. x ⅞" steel pin
K	1	¾* x 1½ x 1½" angle-iron
L	1	⅛ x 1½ x 1½" steel plate
M	1	¾* x 1½ x 3⅜" angle-iron
N	1	⅛ x 1½ x 3⅜" steel plate
O	5	¼"-dia. x 1¼" brass screw and hexnut
P	2	¾"-dia. x 1" hardwood dowel
Q	1	⅜"-dia. x 2" machine bolt with hexnut and two washers

*Cut from one side of a 1½ x 1½" angle-iron.

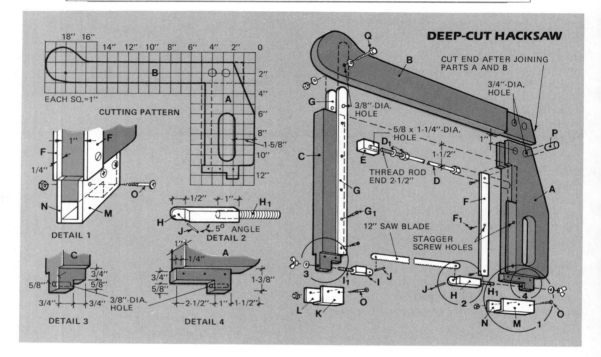

Attach front frame and top frame with a machine bolt (**Q**). Then assemble tension bar and pressure block. Finish saw frame with three coats of wood sealer; apply paste wax to all surfaces.

In use, position the tension bar as close to the blade as possible. The deeper the cut, the higher you must position this bar.

Contour sander

Trying to smooth curved or circular-shaped workpieces by hand sanding is a slow and tedious chore. But the contour sander illustrated will solve that problem by making the finish-sanding of these shapes a quick and easy procedure.

The contour sander features an adjustable handgrip (**A**) and front post (**B**) which hold a cloth-backed abrasive strip.

By adjusting the handgrip and post on the rail

THE HEFTY DEEP-CUT HACKSAW cuts at least twice as deep as a standard hacksaw. The heavy-duty construction of oak and steel ensures many years of service.

(**D**), the abrasive paper will conform to a specific diameter. You can increase the maximum sanding diameter of the tool by substituting a longer abrasive strip and steel rail.

Start by gluing-up the handgrip and post *after* routing a ¼-in.-deep x ½-in. groove in each piece to form the rail channel. Chisel out the recesses for the steel plates (**F**) and make the locking knobs (**G**) by epoxying a ¼-20 bolt into plastic caps from two gallon jugs. Bore and tap threads into the handgrip and post to accept the thumbscrews (**E**).

Bore the two ½-in.-dia. relief holes in the handgrip and post as shown. The holes prevent splitting and provide the spring that's necessary to grip the abrasive strip firmly. Finally, cut the abrasive strip slots into the bottom of the handgrip and post using a dovetail saw or hacksaw.

Apply two coats of polyurethane varnish to all wood surfaces.

MATERIALS LIST—CONTOUR SANDER

Key	No.	Size and description (use)
A	1	1* x 3⅝ x 9¾" oak (handgrip)
B	1	1* x 2 x 5⅝" oak (front post)
C	1	1½ x 2¾ x 2¾" oak (knob)
D	1	½ x ½ x 12" steel keystock (rail)
E	2	¾ x 1½ x 1¾" acrylic (thumbscrew)
E1	2	⅜-16 x 2¾" threaded rod and washer
F	2	¼ x ¾ x 2" steel plate and two 1" No. 8 fh screws
G	2	¾ x 1⅝"-dia. plastic cap
G1	2	¼-20 x ⅞" machine bolt set in epoxy

*Made from gluing-up ½"-thick stock.

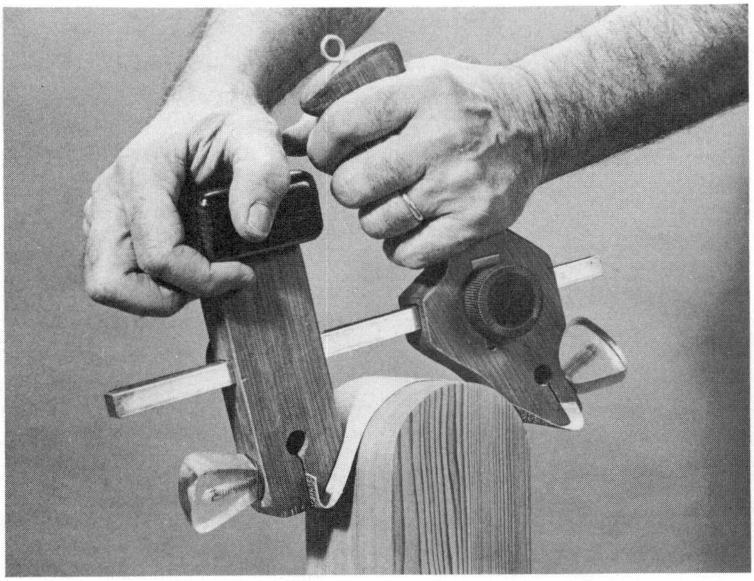

THE FRONT POST and back handle of the contour sander slide on a steel rail to adjust for sanding small-diameter workpieces (left) or for larger pieces (below).

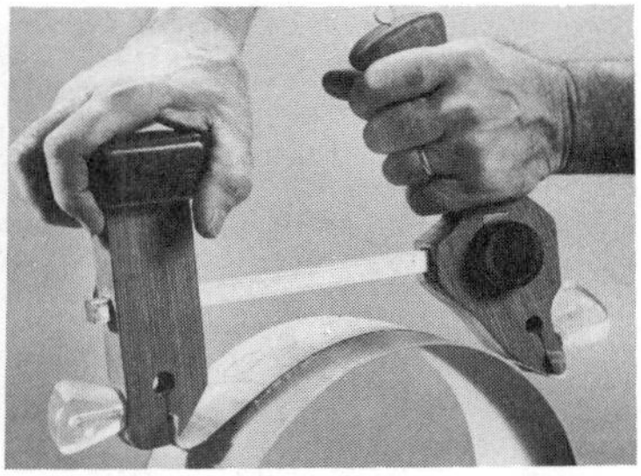

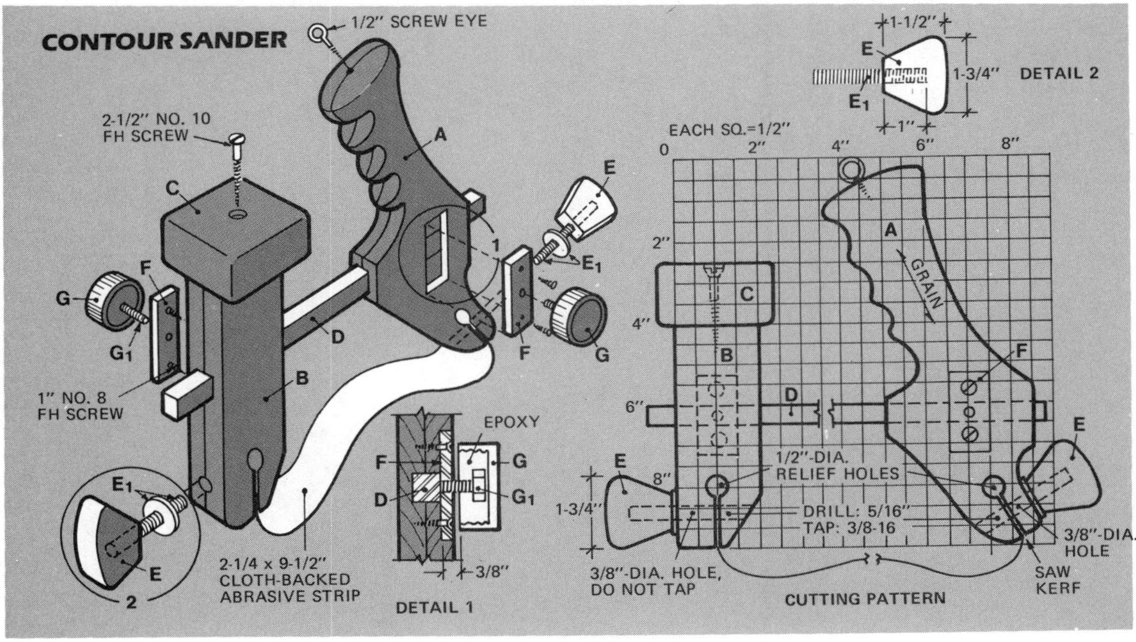
CONTOUR SANDER
1/2" SCREW EYE
2-1/2" NO. 10 FH SCREW
A
B
C
D
E
E1
F
G
G1
1" NO. 8 FH SCREW
2
1
2-1/4 x 9-1/2" CLOTH-BACKED ABRASIVE STRIP
EPOXY
3/8"
DETAIL 1
1-1/2"
1-3/4"
1"
DETAIL 2
EACH SQ.=1/2"
0
2"
4"
6"
8"
GRAIN
1/2"-DIA. RELIEF HOLES
DRILL: 5/16"
TAP: 3/8-16
3/8"-DIA. HOLE, DO NOT TAP
3/8"-DIA. HOLE
SAW KERF
CUTTING PATTERN

Quick-change sander

The simplest of all sanding tools, the sanding block, has just reached state-of-the-art proportions—thanks to the quick-change sander. It features a two-handled grip and a rotating body (**A**) that holds a full 9 x 11-in. sheet of abrasive paper. To eliminate sandpaper waste, all four sides of the body are used. Simply pull the spring-loaded engaging pin (**E**) and rotate the body a quarter of a turn for a fresh sanding surface. There is no need to reposition the abrasive paper.

Cut the body from a 2½-in.-thick solid or glued-up block of hardwood. Carefully sand each side as flat as possible. Then, cut a groove for the clamping rod (**J**). Centerbore a 9/16-in.-dia. hole through the body for the handle shaft (**D**). Shape this shaft by first heating the rod with a propane torch and then, while bending it in a vise, pound the rod with a heavy ball peen hammer. *Caution.* Be sure to wear safety glasses. Cut and shape the handle, knob (**C**) and remaining parts.

Bore and tap the knob and cut matching

USE THE QUICK-CHANGE SANDER for sanding large, flat areas. The body rotates to use each of the four sanding surfaces, without repositioning the abrasive paper.

Key	No.	Size and description (use)
MATERIALS LIST—QUICK-CHANGE SANDER		
A	1	2½ x 2½ x 9″ hardwood (body)
B	1	1½ x 4 x 7″ maple (handle)
C	1	2¼″-dia. maple (knob)
D	1	½″-dia. x 17″ steel rod (shaft)
D1	1	½″-dia. hexnut, washer, 1½″ cotter pin
E	1	3/16″-dia. x 8″ steel rod (engaging pin)
E1	1	½″ brad with ½″-dia. washer (retaining pin)
F	1	¼ x 2 x 2¼″ acrylic or phenolic sheet plastic (front cap)
G	1	½ x 2¼ x 2¼″ hardwood (block)
H	1	¼ x 2¼ x 2¼″ plastic (rear cap)
I	1	3/16 x 1⅜ x 2″ plastic (handle cap)
J	1	¼″-dia. x 10½″ steel rod and wingnut (clamping rod)
K	1	3/16″-dia. x 1½″ threaded rod (pivot rod)
L	1	¼″-dia. x ¾″ rh mach. bolt (shaft lock)
M	1	9 x 10″ thin rubber sheet (backing)
N	11	¾″ No. 6 fh screw
O	4	1″ No. 6 fh screw
P	20	½″ wire nail
Q	1	¼″-dia. x 1½″ compression spring

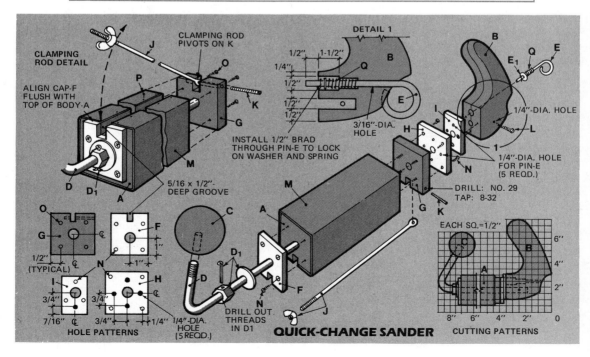

CLAMPING ROD DETAIL

ALIGN CAP-F FLUSH WITH TOP OF BODY-A

CLAMPING ROD PIVOTS ON K

DETAIL 1

INSTALL ½″ BRAD THROUGH PIN-E TO LOCK ON WASHER AND SPRING

3/16″-DIA. HOLE

1/2″ 1-1/2″
1/4″
1/2″
1/2″
1/2″
1/2″

5/16 x 1/2″-DEEP GROOVE

1/4″-DIA. HOLE

1/4″-DIA. HOLE FOR PIN-E (5 REQD.)

DRILL: NO. 29
TAP: 8-32

HOLE PATTERNS
1/2″ (TYPICAL)
3/4″ 3/4″
7/16″ 3/4″ 1/4″
1/4″-DIA. HOLE (5 REQD.)

DRILL OUT THREADS IN D1

QUICK-CHANGE SANDER

EACH SQ.=1/2″
6″
4″
2″
8″ 6″ 4″ 2″ 0

CUTTING PATTERNS

threads on the shaft end. Then bore a stepped hole in the handle for the engaging pin assembly. Three different diameter bits are used. First, bore a hole ½-in.-dia. x 1½ in., then bore a 5/16-in.-dia. x ¾ in. hole (for the compression spring) and finally bore a 3/16-in.-dia. through hole.

Fasten the hardwood block (**G**) and cut and fasten the plastic caps (**F, H**). Make the pivot rod (**D**) by cutting the head from a 3/16-in.-dia. bolt and install it to the clamping rod (**J**) in place. Attach rubber backing (**M**) to the body with contact cement and ½-in. wire nails.

Oak bar clamp

Bar clamps are one accessory that a workshop never seems to have enough of. But now you can make your own oak bar clamps using mostly scrap lumber. The clamp consists of a bar and two jaws—one fixed and one adjustable. Its capacity is limited only by bar length.

First, cut all the parts as shown. Maple is used for the center section of the fixed jaw because it accepts threading well. Also use maple for the clamp pad. Assemble the jaws using glue and ¾-in. brads as shown. Bore a hole in each jaw for the hexhead and eyebolts. To ensure precise alignment of the bar holes, use the adjustable jaw as a drill guide. Hold jaw in place and bore through bar. Repeat every 2 in.

Drill through the nuts on each end of the

MAKE THE OAK BAR CLAMP for gluing stock. Its capacity is limited only by the bar length.

threaded rod. Hammer in a snug-fitting nail on one end to lock the nut in place. Attach the two-piece maple clamping pad around the nut. Bore a 27/64-in.-dia. hole with a ½-13 tap. Screw the rod through the jaw, replace nut and install handle. Finally, apply a clear satin finish.

HERE'S AN ALTERNATIVE TO BUYING expensive metal bar clamps—make your own from scrap wood. Cut several bars of varying lengths for use in clamping work of different sizes.

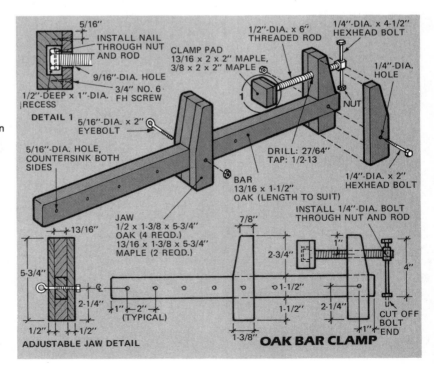

Tools to make for your shop

AS YOU HOLD sander firmly by the knob and handle, you'll find its beefy weight helps you do the work.

Edge sander

A rough edge is usually left on lumber after it's ripped with a saw. An experienced woodworker might choose to plane the edge, but there is an easier way. This edge sander, when used with care, helps you to do professional-quality work.

Use heavy hardwoods, bolts, rods and brass plates to bring your sander in at a hefty 4½ pounds or more. The heavier weight requires less muscle power for downward contact pressure. If it is necessary to "one-hand" the sander, the curved brass bar on top (besides adding some extra weight) directs some of the downward pressure from the back handgrip toward the front of the tool.

Cut the main body block from a well-seasoned piece of maple. We made the side plates from black phenolic plastic, but since this material is expensive and hard to find, you can also use sheet acrylic or any sheet metal.

Cut the handle and front knob from mahogany. The hold-down bolts in the handle and front knob are carriage bolts with their shoulders filed off to allow flush tightening.

Cut a slot for a screwdriver in the top with a hacksaw. Carriage bolts are preferable because

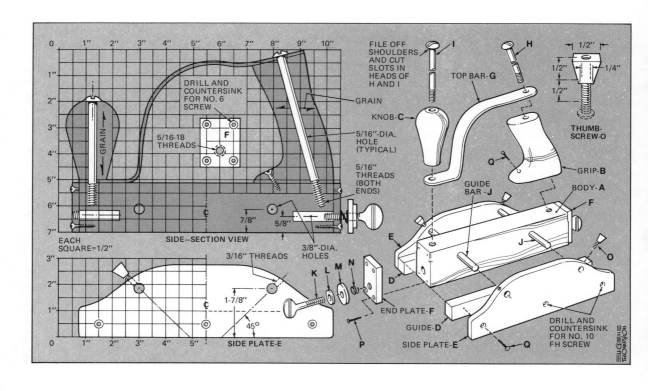

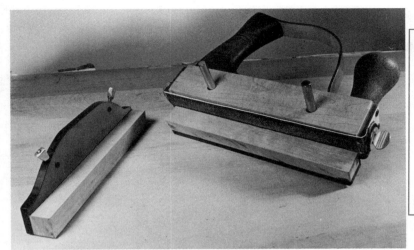

MATERIALS LIST—EDGE SANDER

Key	No.	Size and description (use)
A	1	1¾ × 1⅞ × 9½" maple (body)
B	1	1¼ × 3 × 5" mahogany (grip)
C	1	2"-dia. × 3" mahogany (knob)
D	2	¾ × 1 × 9½" birch (edge guide)
E	2	5/16 × 2¾ × 9½" sheet acrylic (side plate)
F	2	¼ × 1½ × 1⅞" brass (end plate)
G	1	⅛ × 1 × 11½" brass (top bar)
H	1	5/16"-dia. × 6" carriage bolt
I	1	5/16"-dia. × 4" carriage bolt
J	2	⅜"-dia. × 5" steel (guide bar)
K	2	5/16"-dia. × 2" thumbscrew
L	2	⅞"-dia. brass washer
M	2	1¼"-dia. leather washer
N	2	⅜"-dia. compression spring
O	2	¼ × ½ × 1" (thumbscrew)
P	8	1" No. 6 oval-head brass screw
Q	7	1" No. 10 fh steel screw

Misc.: Epoxy, wood finish, metal-buffing materials.

LOOSEN OR REMOVE side plates for easy installation of abrasive paper. Paper must be tightly secured with wingnuts. Any slack will cause paper wear and tear.

they have a larger head and a lower profile than most machine bolts.

Assemble the side plates and birch edge guides and then clamp them to the main body. Now bore the holes for the ⅜-in.-dia. guide bars. This step assures perfect alignment.

The oval screws in the end plates protrude slightly above the surface. This provides two distinct points for the leather washer to bear against so that it can grip the abrasive strips securely.

Because of the limited finger room when the side guides are brought in close to the body of the sander, the thumbscrews must be narrow, yet strong and easy to operate. Make them from ¼-in.-thick brass bar stock and 3/16-in.-dia. bolts. Scribe the shape of the knobs on the bar stock. Then drill and tap before cutting knobs from the bar.

Use epoxy to glue the 3/16-in.-dia. screws into the knobs. Since metal does not have a porous surface to absorb the epoxy, its bond depends on a tough mass that surrounds irregular shapes, and makes them immobile. So, the trick is to create pockets into which the epoxy can run. Grinding or filing irregular notches along the portion of the bolt that is to be threaded into the head creates these epoxy pockets. Polish and buff the knobs and then saw off the heads of the bolts.

Be sure to use brass instead of steel to keep the ⅜-in.-dia. steel guide bars from becoming dimpled. This would allow them to skip out of adjustment and would also cause the travel of the guides to become ragged.

Sheet steel tool

Ground flat stock is sheet steel ground on both sides to produce flatness and a specific thickness such as 0.0625 (1/16 in.) Use this stock to make this handy one-piece tool.

This tool consists of a combination of holes, slots and other useful details: It includes a screwdriver, wrenches for small square and hexagon nuts, gauges for checking rods for ⅛-, ¼- and 5/16-in. diameters; thread chasers for renewing and cleaning 6-32 and 8-32 threads, slots for bending sheet metal and wire, a modest ruler and an edge arrangement for checking 45°, 90° and 135° angles.

First, make a pattern drawing of the tool on self-sticking label paper and apply it to the cleaned surface of your steel blank. Shape the blank and make slots with a milling machine or with hand tools. Drill each hex hole to its bolt diameter and scribe a line around the outer nut for the hexagon shape. Then convert the round hole into a six-sided one with a jeweler's saw and file. Provide the threaded holes with clearance to catch dirt and chips by cutting two opposing notches in each hole with a jeweler's saw.

To make the rule divisions, clamp the blank flat on the compound rest of your lathe and position it to move parallel to the lathe centerline. Then clamp a boring bar in the lathe-headstock collet, with its cutter tip extending downward and pressing lightly against the surface of the tool blank. Space the graduations at 1/16-in. (0.0625 in.) intervals by using the scale on the compound

ATTACH this tool to your key ring and you'll be surprised how handy it is.

USE SMALL hand grinder for smoothing edge at base of screwdriver blade. Finally, remove pattern.

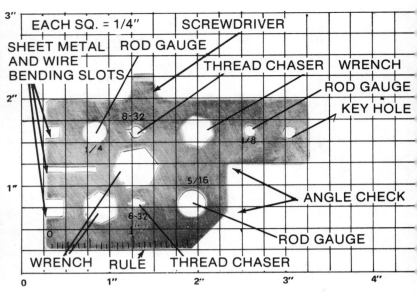

EACH SQ. = 1/4" SCREWDRIVER
SHEET METAL AND WIRE BENDING SLOTS ROD GAUGE THREAD CHASER WRENCH
ROD GAUGE
KEY HOLE
8-32
1/4
1/8
5/16
6-32
ANGLE CHECK
ROD GAUGE
WRENCH RULE THREAD CHASER

feed screw, and engrave by operating the cross-feed screw.

File all tool edges and sand to make them smooth and bring measuring parts to the correct angles. Round corners for comfort in handling.

To harden the tool, heat uniformly to a "cherry red" and then plunge it edgewise into cool water. Polish a small area on one surface to brightness, and then reheat the piece uniformly, over a gas burner, until a straw color appears on the polished spot.

Remove tool immediately from the heat, let it cool, and then polish all over.

ACCESSORY SANDING TABLE

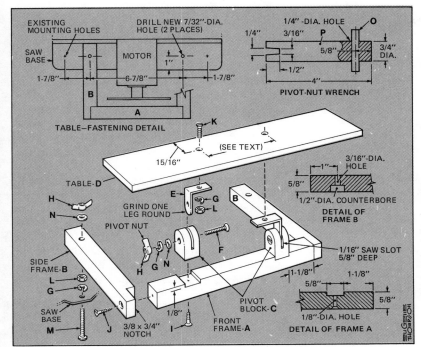

MATERIALS LIST—SANDING TABLE

Key	No.	Size and description (use)
A	1	5/8 × 3/4 × 6 7/8" oak (frame front)
B	2	5/8 × 3/4 × 5 7/8" oak (frame side)
C	2	5/8 × 3/4 × 1" oak (pivot block)
D	1	1/4 × 2 3/8 × 7 5/8" hardwood (table)
E	2	1/2 × 1 × 1" corner brace
F	2	10-24 × 3/4" fh machine screw
G	6	10-24 lockwasher
H	2	10-24 wingnut (pivot nut)
I	2	3/4" No. 6 fh screw
J	2	5/8" No. 4 fh screw
K	2	10-24 × 1/2" fh machine screw
L	4	10-24 hex nut
M	2	10-24 × 1" rh screw
N	4	No. 10 flat washer
O	1	1/4"-dia. × 1 5/8" dowel
P	1	3/4"-dia. × 4" dowel

Misc.: Epoxy.

Accessory sanding table

When you sand small parts such as dollhouse furniture or model fittings, a sanding table is often a necessity for accuracy. The table shown here can be easily made by the hobbyist. Most of the work can be done with a hobbyist's motor tool for which the table is an accessory to the sanding disc.

Use hardwood such as oak and note that all pieces can be cut from a single piece of stock 1x6 x10 in. long. The frame and wood pivots are constructed of pieces 3/4 in. by 5/8 in., and the table is 1/4 in. thick.

Once the pieces are rough-ripped, you can make final cuts with your motor tool. Then cut the 3/8 x 3/4-in. end notches in the frame sides to let in the frame front. The pivot blocks are let into the front frame member in dadoes 1/8 in. deep. Bore holes and cut the slots in the pivot blocks before rounding the tops. Use your corner braces to determine the width of the slot (kerf). The braces should be fairly snug, yet free enough to move within the slot. Attach pivot blocks to front frame member with screws and glue.

Bore the side frame pieces for assembly and counterbore the underneath side to let in the hex nut and lock washer at the saw base. Assemble the frame with screws and glue.

Now, using the dimensions in the drawing, po-

sition and drill one of the holes in the saw base. Attach the frame and use the hole in the other leg to position and bore the second hole. Don't worry if the second hole doesn't fall exactly where it should according to the drawing. Just keep the front frame piece parallel to the sanding disc plane.

Install the corner braces after grinding one leg of each corner brace round. The pivot screws must be locked in place so they won't turn when

ADJUST ANGLE of table with a pivot-nut wrench, as shown here. You make the wrench yourself from a 4-in. length of 3/4-in. dia. dowel. Store it with the table.

the wingnuts are adjusted. You can do this by applying quicksetting epoxy cement over the head of the countersunk screw. To be effective, the holes in the wood pivot blocks should be counterbored sufficiently so the screwhead will be slightly recessed. This will allow the epoxy to grip some wood as well as the screwhead.

Once braces are installed, position and bore the holes in the saw table. If you think that you haven't been too accurate, mount the table frame on the saw base with the sanding disc in place. Then check to be sure you can tilt table as required without coming into contact with the disc.

To adjust the table's angle, you must make a pivot-nut wrench, as shown in the drawing on page 139. The wrench is made from a ¾-in.-dia. length of dowel 4 in. long, and a short piece of ¼-in.-dia. dowel that acts as a finger grip for extra torque. You may make a similar tool of your own design, but be sure you can apply enough pressure on the wingnuts to fix the table securely in place. A slight shift in the table's position could cause problems.

V-block clamp

V-block clamps are simple tools, but they are indispensable for the jobs they do. To make one chuck one end of the stock piece in a lathe and support the other end with a steady rest. Use a conventional cutting-off tool bit to cut a ring from the pipe; make it ⅝ in. long. Then, make a C-segment by cutting a section from the ring to form a gap a few thousandths of an inch wider than the V-block width between its side grooves. Next, mill or file 90° notches at the ends of the C-segment.

At the mid-point of the C-segment, drill a hole with a No. 7 bit and tap for a ¼-20 carriage bolt.

Use a 2-in. carriage bolt threaded its entire length. For ease in turning, drill a ⅛-in.-dia. hole in the square part of the bolt head and fit it with a 2⅛-in. length of steel rod. Cap the ends of the rod with sections cut from ³⁄₁₆-in. aluminum rivets. Drill rivets so they can be press-fitted.

V-BLOCK CLAMPS are indispensable for metal-working projects on tubes and rods. This clamp can be made in a short time and duplicated in various sizes.

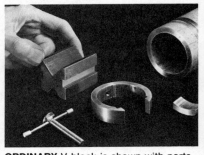

ORDINARY V-block is shown with parts of simple clamp. After ring section is cut from pipe, C-segment is made.

Stand for your propane torch

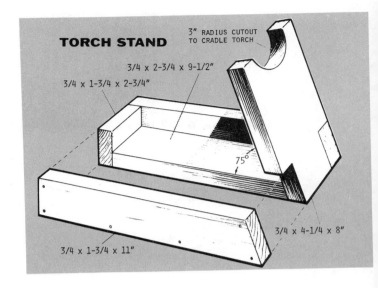

TORCH STAND

3" RADIUS CUTOUT TO CRADLE TORCH

3/4 x 2-3/4 x 9-1/2"

3/4 x 1-3/4 x 2-3/4"

75°

3/4 x 4-1/4 x 8"

3/4 x 1-3/4 x 11"

■ A PROPANE TORCH has an important place in every home workshop, but it is easily tipped over and presents a constant hazard once it is lit. To remedy this, you can construct the simple rack at left. It holds the torch at a convenient angle and leaves both hands free. In addition, when the torch is not in use it can remain in the stand for storage. The torch can be readily lifted out when desired and the tray in the base provides handy storage for the lighter, solder, flux and other torch-related items.

All parts of nominal one-inch stock and assembly is with glue and 4d finishing nails. You may want to build several stands, altering the angle of the rest so that the torch can be used for special jobs. If you decide to make a rest that will hold the torch nearer to the vertical, notch the small board at the other end in order to cradle the tank bottom securely.

If desired, you can add a torch stand as a permanent fixture to your workbench by attaching it with a large flathead screw. You can turn stand to whatever direction is most convenient for the job at hand.

WEAR SAFETY GOGGLES

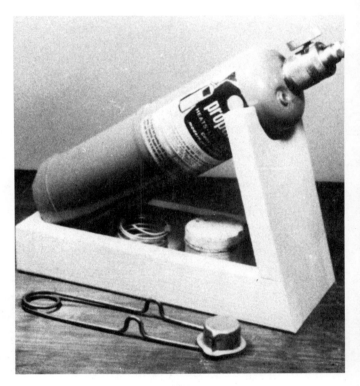

Tools that will surprise you

PICTURE-FRAMING TOOLS

Miter trimmer. After you make a cut with a saw and miterbox, the massive hollow ground blades of this miter trimmer cut like a razor to produce an accurate finish cut that is glass smooth and requires no sanding. A left and a right gauge lock into any angle you desire from 45° to 90° to guide an angled cut. You can use the trimmer on stock up to 4 in. wide when mitering. You can also use it to square ends on stock up to 6 in. wide.

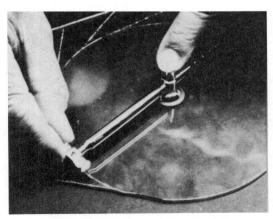

Circle glass cutter. The circle glass cutter cuts up to 10½-in.-dia. disks for picture frames, mirrors, clocks and flashlights. Hold the rubber pivot firmly in the center of the glass and rotate the cutter head in a circle. Next, adjust the cutter head for straight cuts and make tangential cuts from the circle to the edge of the glass. Break off the pieces formed and you have a perfect glass disk. The cutter comes with three spare cutting wheels and a screwdriver.

Brad pusher. This lever-assisted brad pusher makes setting the smallest brads a fast, simple and accurate task. You can drive brads without bending them, damaging your fingers or marring the workpiece. It's especially handy for setting the small brads that hold the backing in a picture frame. One jaw padded with rubber protects the frame while the other jaw presses in the brad. The pusher works on molding up to 1¾ in. deep x 3½ in. wide.

WOODWORKING TOOLS

Block plane. This superb small plane from West Germany is available now in the United States. For the same price you'd expect to pay for a first-rate steel plane, you can now enjoy the feel of working with an all-wood one. Its 2¹⁄₁₆ x 5⅞-in. body is crafted of varnished-steamed beech and the bottom plate is of hornbeam. Surprisingly, the block plane features a depth adjustment knob—no more tapping the blade to depth with a hammer.

Saw rasp. This Japanese saw rasp planes and shapes wood smoothly and quickly without clogging. It's made of 10 two-sided hacksaw blades assembled so the fine teeth are on one side of the rasp and the coarse teeth are on the other. The overall cutting surface is 1¼ x 10¼ in. To change sides for use, loosen the knurled nut on top and reposition the handle. The round knob gives you an extra hold for two-handed leverage.

Spokeshave. This round-face spokeshave works like a plane to smooth concave surfaces. Adjusting screws allow setting for thickness of shaving and provide lateral positioning. Normally, you would set the blade almost flush with the sole. Work with the grain to prevent tearing the wood on curves.

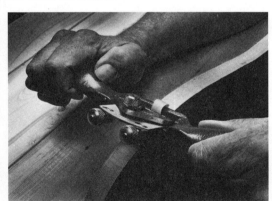

Hold-down clamp. You can install this handy hold-down clamp anywhere on your bench by simply boring and counterboring a hole and installing a hold-down bolt. The clamp slides onto the bolt head ready to secure work that's up to 3 in. thick. The clamp rotates 360° around the holding bolt to secure work at the right spot or easiest angle for the hobbyist. When it's no longer needed, remove the clamp and let the hold-down bolt drop down out of the way.

Cabinet scrapers. With this set of cabinet scrapers, you'll be able to smooth hollows and convex shapes as well as flat surfaces—nearly every shape you'll encounter in the workshop. The set includes a gooseneck 2¾ x 4¾ in., a round-end 2 x 5¾ in. and a straight scraper 2⅜ x 5⅞ in. Besides scraping paper-thin shavings to smooth wood, you can remove paint and fillers in hard-to-reach parts of moldings and in other irregular surfaces.

Brad driver. The wood-handled brad driver has a magnetic barrel that picks up a brad (inset photo), drives and sets it. The tool drives up to 1-in., 16- to 19-ga. brads. It is invaluable for paneling jobs, where one hand holds the panel while the other picks up and secures the brad. It's also handy when constructing picture frames, fastening window screens, applying decorative molding and working on miniatures and models. You can find many other uses.

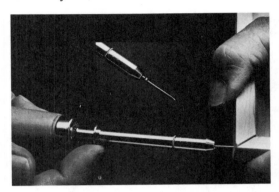

Hole cutter. Finally, there's a hole cutter claimed by its maker to work in a portable electric drill—and it does. The cutter removes disks from 1½ to 18 in. in diameter in wood, plastic and soft metals. You can make portholes and speaker or basin cutouts in wood or plastic laminate, to name a few uses. Push the free end clockwise to get a clean hole (cutout); push it counterclockwise to cut a clean disk. Cutter includes a steel case, a bit and an Allen wrench.

Countersink/counterbore bits. There's a tapered bit for boring holes that conform to the shape of a screw. Each bit comes with a matched fitted stop collar and countersink/counterbore. In one operation you can prepare the wood for the threads, the screwhead and a wood plug. A setscrew, adjusted with the included Allen wrench, secures the stop collar in position to counterbore for a plug or countersink for a screwhead.

Toolbox classics you can build

■ A TRIP TO AN ANTIQUE FAIR or shop is almost certain to turn up one or more old toolboxes. They are still around in a variety of shapes and forms—from the rare master craftsman's box made of hardwood that seems to accommodate every tool imaginable to a simple carpenter's pine box like the one shown.

The majority of old toolboxes we were fortunate enough to find were obviously crafted by their owner-users. Typically, the design details were kept simple and the boxes were extremely functional.

OPEN CARPENTER'S toolbox is handy for conventional carpentry tools or to display magazines.

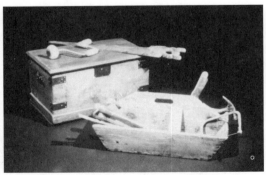

BOTH ORIGINAL toolboxes were found in Wheeling, WV, antique shops. They are good examples of carpenter design—built by their owners.

OUR LIDDED REPRODUCTION is crafted of ½- and ¾-in. cherry; we added a tray for chisels and such.

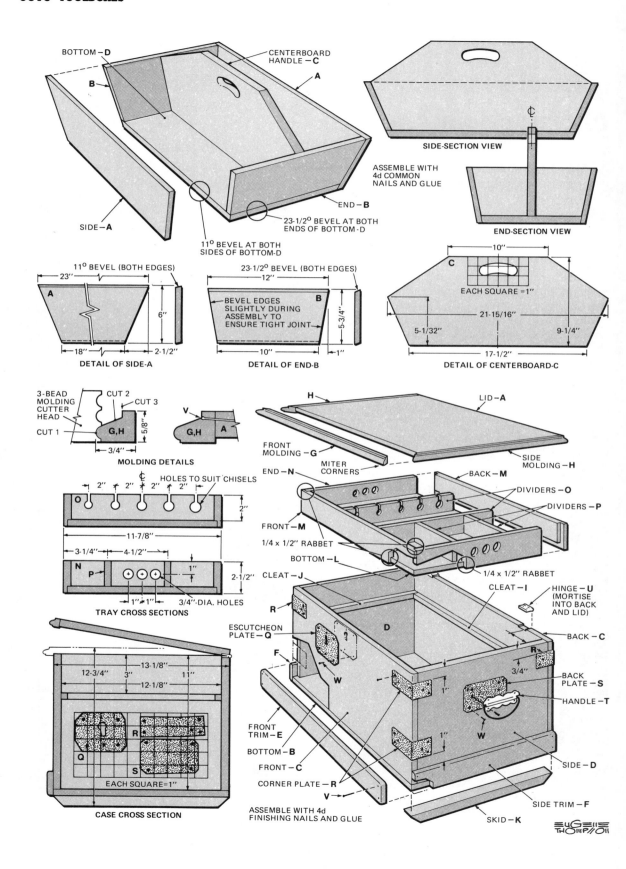

BOTTOM – **D**

CENTERBOARD HANDLE – **C**

A

B

SIDE-SECTION VIEW

SIDE – **A**

END – **B**

23-1/2° BEVEL AT BOTH ENDS OF BOTTOM-D

11° BEVEL AT BOTH SIDES OF BOTTOM-D

ASSEMBLE WITH 4d COMMON NAILS AND GLUE

END-SECTION VIEW

11° BEVEL (BOTH EDGES)
23″
A
6″
18″
2-1/2″

DETAIL OF SIDE-A

23-1/2° BEVEL (BOTH EDGES)
12″
BEVEL EDGES SLIGHTLY DURING ASSEMBLY TO ENSURE TIGHT JOINT
B
5-3/4″
10″
1″

DETAIL OF END-B

10″
C
EACH SQUARE =1″
21-15/16″
5-1/32″
9-1/4″
17-1/2″

DETAIL OF CENTERBOARD-C

3-BEAD MOLDING CUTTER HEAD
CUT 2
CUT 3
CUT 1
G,H
5/8″
3/4″

V
G,H
A

MOLDING DETAILS

HOLES TO SUIT CHISELS
2″ 2″ 2″ 2″
O
2″
11-7/8″
3-1/4″
4-1/2″
N
P
1″
2-1/2″
1″ 1″
3/4″-DIA. HOLES

TRAY CROSS SECTIONS

12-3/4″
13-1/8″
3″
11″
12-1/8″
R
Q
S
EACH SQUARE=1″

CASE CROSS SECTION

H
LID – **A**
FRONT MOLDING – **G**
MITER CORNERS
SIDE MOLDING – **H**
END – **N**
BACK – **M**
DIVIDERS – **O**
DIVIDERS – **P**
FRONT – **M**
1/4 x 1/2″ RABBET
BOTTOM – **L**
1/4 x 1/2″ RABBET
CLEAT – **J**
CLEAT – **I**
HINGE – **U** (MORTISE INTO BACK AND LID)
R
BACK – **C**
ESCUTCHEON PLATE – **Q**
D
3/4″
R
F
BACK PLATE – **S**
1″
HANDLE – **T**
W
W
FRONT TRIM – **E**
1″
BOTTOM – **B**
SIDE – **D**
FRONT – **C**
SIDE TRIM – **F**
CORNER PLATE – **R**
V
SKID – **K**

ASSEMBLE WITH 4d FINISHING NAILS AND GLUE

EUGENE THOMPSON

THE ORIGINAL HANDLES were probably handcrafted by the box's journeyman builder. A search of old hardware catalogs failed to turn up any that had the same look so we created our own.

WE CREATED our version using available hardware-store handles and a backup plate fashioned from 28-gauge sheet metal. Metal parts are painted with flat-black latex and coated with varnish.

The closed box is the more elaborate of the two; the original is made of ½- and ¾-in. stock (pine and maple). It was severely distressed when we found it with many nicks and gouges in the pine. We created the copy in the same thicknesses and, for sheer good looks, opted to use cherry for the case and mahogany for the tray. These hardwoods not only add beauty but also strength and durability.

The inside tray was missing from the original so we crafted our own version to accommodate

THIS END VIEW of the box shows the severe distressing that exists on the original. It's important that you resist the urge to overdo it when putting "antique" marks on your reproduction.

our needs. The result is a tray sized to suit my collection of fine chisels. You can, of course, alter the members' shapes and locations to suit the tools that you plan to store in the tray. Careful design and planning before you begin will result in having the tools where you want them when you are working on a project. Or, if you choose to use the toolbox as a coffee table with storage, eliminate the small partitions completely so that the tray can be used as a server.

Making the box with the lid

The cherry for the box is available from any mail order distributor or lumberyard that stocks hardwood. Use our materials list to prepare your order. The hardware is hand-fashioned, using 28-gauge sheet metal as described later in the building instructions. All metal parts can be purchased at your local hardware store.

Start by laying out all parts according to the dimensions in the drawing. Use a square to ensure accurate cuts and cut all the parts to size. The wide boards for the top and bottom can be created by edge-joining narrow boards. For the original, the boards were joined using ¼-in. dowels in the joint, and ½-in. corrugated fasteners in both ends across the joint.

Moldings made with handtools

Notice the decorative edging on the lid. This apparently was the journeyman's way of "showing off" his skills. The original moldings, in all likelihood, were fashioned using handtools. Though we did some of the shaping with power tools, we, too, had to resort to hand work to closely match the original molding shape.

Start by cutting the three molding pieces to width, depth and length. Then, set up your table saw with the molding cutterhead shown. You *must* use an auxiliary wooden fence to make the cut as shown in the drawing.

You should also use both a hold-down and a hold-in to avoid any chance of accident to yourself when making the moldings. This will also result in greater accuracy. Make the initial pass over the cutterheads to achieve the first stage. Finish shaping the molding by using a block plane with razor-sharp iron, files and sandpaper. (*Note:* You can substitute the Surform Shaver hand rasp for the block plane with great success.)

Installing the moldings

When the moldings are shaped and smoothed to your satisfaction, they can be installed on the three required edges (there is none along the back edge). To do it, predrill lead holes through the moldings or you will split them. Use 1-in. No. 18 brads and glue to affix the moldings.

Predrill hole for nails

Like the original, all joinery here is with nails and glue. To prevent any chance of splitting, predrill lead holes for the nails. You actually need two different-size holes for your nails. They should slide freely through the first piece, and then be driven into the leadholes in the second.

We used fewer nails than in the original because it is apparent that many of them were driven over the years to correct loose or split boards (see photo). You do want *some* nails to show and give it an antiqued look; in these spots use 3d or 4d common nails. Set the heads slightly below the surface. The balance of the fastening is done with almost-invisible 4d finishing nails.

The tray

We used mahogany to fashion our tray and laid it out as shown to suit the author's tools. The interior members can be resized and reshaped to suit the use to which you will put the tray. Assemble the tray using glue and 4d finishing nails. Once again, take care to align the pieces correctly and predrill to prevent splitting. Finish by locating and installing the shelf cleats on the case members.

Sand all parts before assembly, finishing up with 150-grit abrasive, and assemble the box. The next day, attach the lid to the case using the pair of 1-in. hinges set in mortises as shown.

Homemade corner irons

The corner "irons" are, in reality, cut from 28-gauge sheet metal. You can cut and shape them at this time, but *do not* install them yet.

It is important that you notice that these pieces of "hardware" are *not* cut perfectly even. We copied the "off" sizes, shapes and locations of the originals exactly. After cutting the pieces, file off any burrs and bore the holes for the escutcheon pins. After bending the corner pieces, paint them with flat black latex (after neutralizing the sheet metal with vinegar).

Finish shaping the escutcheon plate for the "keyhole" and temporarily position the plate on the box. Mark the wood for the keyhole, remove the plate and gouge out the keyhole. Since you won't actually install a lock, you needn't bore through for any hardware. Gouge it out with a small chisel or knife, and paint the hole black.

Use commercial handle

We made a look-alike handle by using a commercially available handle and cutting the backplate from 28-gauge sheet metal. The photographs show how closely the reproduction resembles the original.

The box shown was finished by staining with maple stain thinned about 50 percent with turpentine. After dusting off the piece, apply the stain with either brush or rag. Let the stain set several minutes, then wipe off all excess. Allow the box to dry overnight.

Next day, after wiping the box with a tack cloth, seal with a coat of clear (water white) shellac thinned 50 percent with denatured alcohol.

MATERIALS LIST—OPEN TOOLBOX

Key	No.	Size and description (use)
A	2	½ x 6 x 23″ pine (side)
B	2	½ x 5¾ x 12″ pine (end)
C	1	¾ x 9¼ x 21 15/16″ pine (centerboard)
D	1	¾ x 10 x 18⅝″ pine (bottom)

MATERIALS LIST—LIDDED TOOLBOX

Key	No.	Size and description (use)
A	1	½ x 13⅛ x 22″ cherry (lid)
B	1	½ x 13⅛ x 22″ cherry (bottom)
C	2	½ x 11 x 22″ cherry (front/back)
D	2	½ x 11 x 12⅛″ cherry (side)
E	1	½ x 1⅞ x 23″ cherry (front trim)
F	2	½ x 1⅞ x 13⅛″ cherry (side trim)
G	1	⅝ x ¾ x 23½″ cherry (front molding)
H	2	⅝ x ¾ x 13⅞″ cherry (side molding)
I	2	½ x ½ x 20″ cherry (cleat)
J	2	½ x ½ x 12⅛″ cherry (side cleat)
K	2	¾ x 1 x 13⅛″ cherry (skid)
L	1	½ x 11⅜ x 20¼″ mahogany (tray bottom)
M	2	½ x 2½ x 20¾″ mahogany (tray front/back)
N	2	½ x 2½ x 11⅜″ mahogany (tray side)
O	2	½ x 2½ x 10⅞″ mahogany (divider)
P	2	½ x 2 x 6¼″ mahogany (divider)
Q	1	28-ga. x 3 x 4″ sheet metal (escutcheon plate)
R	6	28-ga. x 1½ x 4¾″ sheet metal (corner plate)
S	2	28-ga. x 2⅝ x 4¼″ sheet metal (back plate)
T	2	1¾ x 3½″ chest handle
U	2	1 x 1¾″ butt hinge
V		4d finishing nails
W		¾″ roundhead escutcheon pins cut to ⅜″

Allow the box to dry overnight. When dry, sand lightly with 180-grit paper wrapped around a cushioned sanding block. When it's smooth, dust off and wipe with a tack rag.

You can now attach the flat black "hardware." Fasten the corner braces and all three escutcheon plates using brass escutcheon pins. We used ¾-in. pins, which we nipped to ⅜-in. length using a diagonal cutter. The escutcheon pin heads must also be touched up with the flat black latex paint.

Install the handles over the plates, putting the screws (that come in the package) into predrilled holes. When all the hardware is in place—and the black paint is absolutely dry—apply a coat of varnish to all parts as it comes from the can. Allow the piece to dry thoroughly before using.

Making the open box

The open box is easier to recreate. However, that doesn't mean sloppy work is acceptable. Do it the professional way: Start by rough-cutting the six boards to approximate, but slightly over, sizes.

When all parts are cut, you can lay out the angles accurately, using a bevel square. Start by laying out the angles for cutting the ends of the sides. Cut the ends of both sides at the same time, or use a clamped stop block on your radial-saw table so that both sides will be identical in length. Next, repeat the procedure to cut the miters on the ends of the endpieces. Again, cut both at one time or use a clamped stop block. Once the endpieces are cut, you can use your bevel square to transfer the angle so that the bottoms of the sides and ends will be ripped parallel to the bottom board.

At this stage, tack-fasten the boards together to check all bevel and miter cuts. Make adjustments if necessary; overall size, after all, is not critical.

Remember that you will need bevel cuts on all four edges of the bottom piece, and along the edges of the end boards where they butt the side pieces. These are easily determined with the pieces tack-joined. When sides, ends and bottom are fitted to your satisfaction, sand all boards smooth, finishing up with 150-grit abrasive paper.

Assembling with glue and nails

Assemble the case, using carpenter's glue and 3d common nails. Again, do it professionally and first assemble the box using a bare minimum of 3d *finishing* nails and clamps. You will need a pair of mitered boards, for use as pads, with each clamp. These let you draw the boards tightly together. When the box is assembled and clamped, set it aside to dry. The next day, remove the clamps and add the 3d common nails. Set all nailheads slightly below the surface.

When the box is assembled, use your bevel square to lay out the centerboard (handle). Make a test cut in scrap and, when satisfied with the angle joint, lay out and cut the board itself. The hand-hold cutout is centered on the board and can be made quickly by boring a 1-in.-dia. hole at each end and finishing the cut with either sabre or coping saw. Sand the board and install it in the case using carpenter's glue and 3d common nails.

Don't overdo distressing

The original box is quite battered and distressed. We deliberately held the distress marks on the reproduction to a minimum. Overdistressing is often the mark of a neophyte finisher. A few dents or bangs here and there with a ballpeen hammer, perhaps a gouge or two with a carver's chisel, the exposed nails, plus a few punctures with awl or file tang will do.

Dust the box off and wipe it with a tack rag. Then, to ensure an even stain finish, apply boiled linseed oil to all exposed end grains. Immediately apply the oil stain of your choice and wipe off excess.

Set the piece aside to dry overnight. Next day, sand lightly with 180-grit paper; dust off and wipe with a tack rag. Apply a coat of varnish thinned 50 percent with turpentine. Let the box dry 24 hours.

Next, using an artist's pointed brush, apply burnt umber pigment from a tube, thinned as needed with turpentine, to all nailheads and to small distress marks (punctures). The idea is to simulate years of accumulated dirt. Allow the umber to dry overnight, sand the piece lightly with 220-grit paper, dust and wipe with a tack rag.

Finish by applying a coat of varnish as it comes from the can.

To achieve a hand-rubbed, waxed look, we used satin finish varnish on the boxes shown.

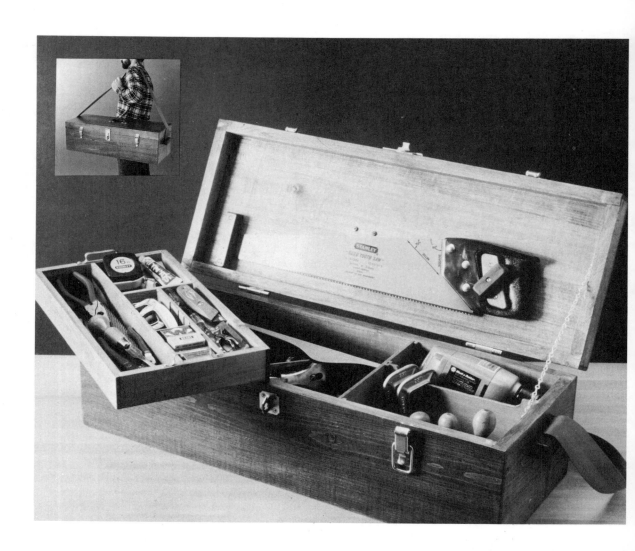

Portable tool-boxes

■ A CARPENTER'S TOOLBOX must protect and house all the basic hand tools, yet be compact enough to be carried to the job site. Unfortunately, most store-bought toolboxes are either too big or too small. Here are plans for building two toolboxes that combine adequate storage with portability. And both designs can be altered easily to accommodate your tool collection and work requirements. The carry-all tool chest is an

updated version of the boxes used by house builders around the turn of the century. The saw-horse toolbox is an open box with legs that stow underneath.

CARRY-ALL TOOL CHEST

This is an updated version of a carpenter's tool chest which was popular more than 90 years ago. The original was much larger and, therefore, less portable than our scaled-down model.

The chest is dimensioned to give the maximum tool storage without sacrificing portability. The measurements can be altered easily to accommodate your specific needs. The tool chest length is generally determined by what size handsaw is stored in the lid. The chest shown houses a 20-in. saw.

Assembly

Build the chest from ¾-in. poplar. Pine or cypress would also be suitable. Note that the lift-out tool tray parts are resawed to 5/16- and ½-in. thick. Also keep in mind that the tool chest is assembled as a solid box, then the lid is cut from the chest on a table saw.

Start by cutting the chest top, ends, bottom, front and back. Form the 11½-in.-wide top by edge-gluing two boards together. Be certain to cut the front, back and end pieces 9⅜ in. wide to allow for the ⅛ in. of wood removed by the saw blade when the lid is cut.

After sawing the chest parts to size, cut the rabbet joints, as shown, using a router and a rabbeting bit. Rabbet the tool chest front and back on three edges, the end pieces on the bottom edge

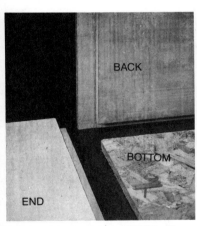

ASSEMBLE THE TOOL CHEST with rabbet joints. Note that the back is rabbeted on two edges to receive the bottom and tool chest end. Rabbet the end on bottom edge only.

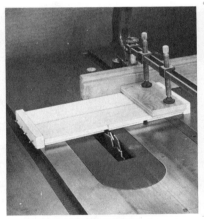

THIS TIME-SAVING SETUP allows you to dado both tool tray end pieces simultaneously. Nail wood blocks across both ends to prevent shifting and to ensure alignment.

AFTER ASSEMBLING THE TOOL CHEST, screw bottom panel in place. Use wedges to obtain more pressure from nylon band clamp.

ATTACH T-HINGES about 4½ in. from each end of the toolbox. Use several pieces of masking tape to keep toolbox lid in place.

MAKE SHOULDER STRAP from seatbelt material. To prevent the strap from fraying, heat-seal ends with a soldering gun.

THE HANDSAW HOLDER feature was saved from the original tool chest design. Custom-cut handle block and turn-button to fit saw.

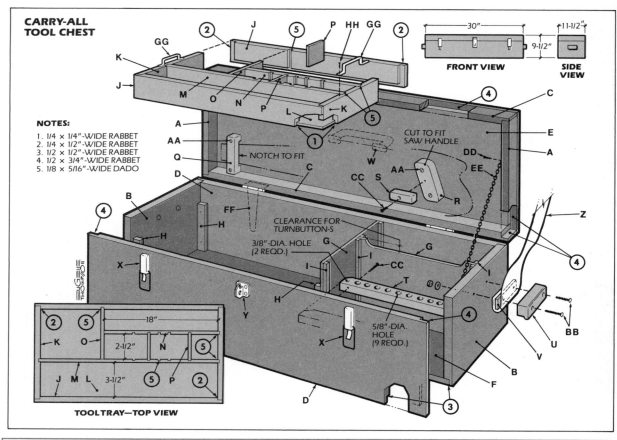

CARRY-ALL TOOL CHEST

NOTES:
1. 1/4 × 1/4"-WIDE RABBET
2. 1/4 × 1/2"-WIDE RABBET
3. 1/2 × 1/2"-WIDE RABBET
4. 1/2 × 3/4"-WIDE RABBET
5. 1/8 × 5/16"-WIDE DADO

FRONT VIEW — 30", 9-1/2"

SIDE VIEW — 11-1/2"

NOTCH TO FIT

CLEARANCE FOR TURNBUTTON-S

3/8"-DIA. HOLE (2 REQD.)

CUT TO FIT SAW HANDLE

5/8"-DIA. HOLE (9 REQD.)

TOOL TRAY—TOP VIEW — 18", 2-1/2", 3-1/2"

MATERIALS LIST—CARRY-ALL TOOL CHEST						
Key	**No.**	**Size and description (use)**				
A	2	3/4 × 1 3/4 × 11'' poplar (lid end)	J	2	1/2 × 2 1/4 × 18 1/8'' poplar (tray front and back)
B	2	3/4 × 7 1/2 × 11'' poplar (chest end)	K	2	1/2 × 2 1/4 × 9 3/8'' poplar (tray end)
C	2	3/4 × 1 3/4 × 30'' poplar (lid front and back)	L	1	1/4 × 9 3/8 × 17 5/8'' lauan plywood (tray bottom)
D	2	3/4 × 7 1/2 × 30'' poplar (chest front and back)	M	1	5/16 × 2 × 17 3/8'' poplar (divider)
E	1	3/4 × 11 1/2 × 30'' poplar (top)	N	1	5/16 × 2 × 11 1/8'' poplar (divider)
F	1	7/16 × 11 × 29 1/2'' flake board (bottom)	O	1	5/16 × 2 × 5 3/16'' poplar (divider)
G	2	1/4 × 6 5/8 × 9 7/8'' lauan plywood (divider)	P	2	5/16 × 2 × 2 3/4'' hardboard (adjustable divider)
H	4	1/2 × 3/4 × 4 3/4'' poplar (corner post)	Q	1	3/4 × 1 × 4'' poplar (saw blade holder)
I	6	5/16 × 5/16 × 7'' poplar·(cleat)	R	1	1 1/8 × 1 1/8 × 4'' poplar (handle block)
			S	1	5/8 × 1 × 2 1/2'' poplar (turnbutton)
			T	1	3/4 × 1 1/4 × 9 1/2'' poplar (tool rack)
			U	2	1 × 1 1/4 × 4'' oak (handle)
			V	2	1/4 × 1 × 4'' hardboard (strap cleat)
			W	1	plastic luggage handle
			X	2	1 1/4 × 3 1/2'' pull-down chest latch
			Y	1	3 1/2'' latching safety hasp
			Z	1	2 × 70'' nylon seat belt strap
			AA	4	1 1/4'' No. 6 fh screw
			BB	4	1/4''-dia. × 2 1/2'' fh bolt, washer and nut
			CC	3	1 3/4'' No. 10 fh screw
			DD	2	3/4'' No. 8 rh screw
			EE	1	12'' chain
			FF	2	4'' T-hinge
			GG	2	1/16 × 1/2 × 5'' steel (tray handle)
			HH	4	1/2'' No. 6 rh screw

and the top on all four edges. Next, assemble the box with glue and 1¼-in. finishing nails. Allow the glue to dry overnight, then sand all sides of the box smooth using a belt and finishing sander.

Cutting off the lid

Set the table saw fence for a 2-in.-wide cut. It's important that the saw blade and fence be per-

fectly parallel. Otherwise, the start and finish point of the cut will not meet evenly.

Start cutting with the chest standing on end and the top against the fence. Cut the end and then saw through the front. Cut the other end and, finally, through the back. *Caution:* Always cut clear through each side; *never* roll the box back onto the saw blade. On the final cut that frees the lid from the box, use a stick to push the

CUT THE TOOLBOX ENDS 1-in. over-sized with a portable circular saw. Use a fine-tooth saw blade to prevent splintering the veneer. Move to table saw for final trimming.

TRIM THE EDGES of each end piece with the blade angled 4° and miter gauge set at 21°. Orient the 4° bevels so that the inside surface is wider than the outside face.

TRIM SPACER TOPS with blade set at 7°. Note that an auxiliary fence is clamped to the saw fence to stabilize workpiece.

WHEN CUTTING the ¼-in.-wide dadoes for the toolbox bottom, be certain that dadoes align in the corners of the box (arrow).

BORE ½-IN.-DIA. HOLES in the toolbox ends to accept hardwood dowels. The dowels provide solid wood for driving in screws.

PARTIALLY ASSEMBLED toolbox is shown with the left leg guide screwed to end. Right leg guide stands in dado cut in box side.

lid beyond the spinning saw blade. Now, place the lid on the chest and check for any wobbling or unevenness. Knock down any high spots with a sanding block and 80-grit abrasive paper.

Next, make the two removable interior partitions from ¼-in. plywood. Note that one partition is cut down to provide clearance for the turnbutton which holds the handsaw in place.

Cut the pieces needed to make the lift-out tool tray. Arrange the tray dividers to accommodate your tools. Then, nail four corner posts inside the chest to support the tool tray. Now, custom-cut the three parts that form the holder for your handsaw. Screw each part to the lid underside while holding the handsaw in position.

Finish-sand and stain all wood surfaces. Next, install the two 4-in. T-hinges about 4½ in. from each end. If you build a chest more than 36 in. long, add a third, middle hinge. Now, screw the chain lid support in place. Install a safety latching hasp and two chest latches.

Next, make the 2-in.-wide shoulder strap from automobile seat-belt material, available at most auto parts stores and auto seat cover shops. To install the strap, first cut two oak handles for each end of the chest. Then, wrap the strap around a ¼-in. hardboard spacer and bolt through the handle, belt and spacer. To complement the shoulder strap, add a 5-in. luggage handle to the top, center of the lid.

Finish all wood surfaces, inside and out, with three coats of polyurethane varnish.

SAWHORSE TOOLBOX

This cleverly designed project combines a compact toolbox and a sturdy sawhorse in one portable package. Four hardwood legs are stored neatly in the shallow cavity under the toolbox. To set up the sawhorse, slide the legs into the channels built in the toolbox ends.

Build the toolbox from ash-veneer plywood and ash hardwood. The 29-in.-long toolbox is shown with 26-in. legs—the longest legs this

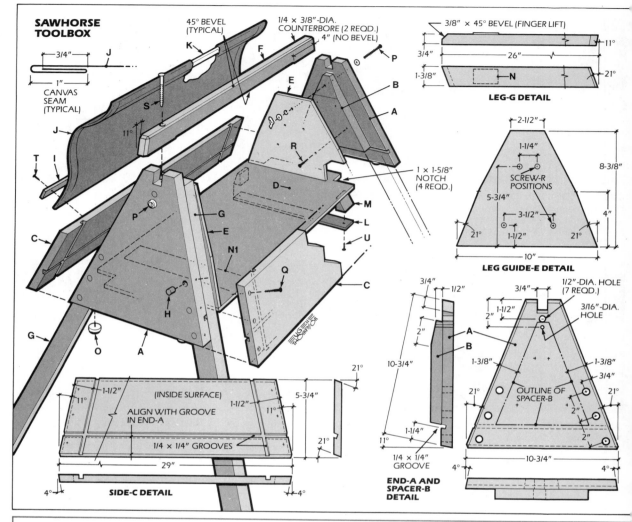

SAWHORSE TOOLBOX

45° BEVEL (TYPICAL)

1/4 × 3/8"-DIA. COUNTERBORE (2 REQD.) 4" (NO BEVEL)

3/4"

1"

CANVAS SEAM (TYPICAL)

11°

1 × 1-5/8" NOTCH (4 REQD.)

3/8" × 45° BEVEL (FINGER LIFT)

26"

3/4"

1-3/8"

11°

21°

N

LEG-G DETAIL

2-1/2"

1-1/4"

8-3/8"

SCREW-R POSITIONS

5-3/4"

3-1/2"

21°

1-1/2"

21°

4"

10"

LEG GUIDE-E DETAIL

(INSIDE SURFACE)

ALIGN WITH GROOVE IN END-A

1-1/2"

11°

1-1/2"

11°

5-3/4"

21°

1/4 × 1/4" GROOVES

29"

21°

4°

4°

SIDE-C DETAIL

3/4"

1/2"

3/4"

1/2"-DIA. HOLE (7 REQD.)

3/16"-DIA. HOLE

1-1/2"

2"

2"

10-3/4"

A

B

1-3/8"

OUTLINE OF SPACER-B

1-3/8"

3/4"

21°

21°

21°

2"

11°

1-1/4"

2"

10-3/4"

1/4 × 1/4" GROOVE

4°

4°

END-A AND SPACER-B DETAIL

MATERIALS LIST—SAWHORSE TOOLBOX

Key	No.	Size and description (use)
A	2	$\frac{3}{4}$ × 11"*-wide × 12"* ash veneer plywood (end)
B	2	$\frac{3}{4}$ × 9"*-wide × 11"* ash veneer plywood (spacer)
C	2	$\frac{1}{2}$ × $5\frac{3}{4}$ × 29" ash veneer plywood (side)
D	1	$\frac{1}{4}$ × 11" × 30"* ash veneer plywood (bottom)
E	2	$\frac{1}{4}$ × $8\frac{3}{8}$ × 10" ash veneer plywood (leg guide)
F	1	$\frac{3}{4}$ × $1\frac{1}{2}$ × 29" ash (handle)
G	4	$\frac{3}{4}$ × $1\frac{3}{8}$ × 26" ash (leg)
H	14	$\frac{1}{2}$"-dia. × $^{11}/_{16}$" hardwood dowel
I	1	$\frac{1}{4}$ × $\frac{3}{4}$ × $23\frac{1}{4}$" ash (cover retainer)
J	1	$16\frac{1}{2}$ × $25\frac{1}{2}$" canvas (dust cover)
K	1	$\frac{1}{4}$ × $\frac{1}{2}$ × 21" steel (weight strip)
L	1	$\frac{1}{8}$ × $1\frac{1}{4}$ × $10^9/_{16}$" aluminum (leg retainer)
M	2	$\frac{3}{4}$ × 1 × $1\frac{1}{2}$" poplar (mounting block)
N	4	1 × $2\frac{1}{2}$" Velcro fastener (leg strip)
N1	1	2 × 9" Velcro fastener (box strip)
O	4	$\frac{3}{4}$"-dia. furniture glide
P	2	$^3/_{16}$"-dia. × $2\frac{1}{2}$" fh machine screw, wing nut, finish washer and lockwasher
Q	12	$1\frac{1}{2}$" No. 10 fh screw
R	8	$1\frac{1}{4}$" No. 8 fh screw
S	2	$2\frac{1}{4}$" No. 12 fh screw
T	5	$\frac{1}{2}$" No. 6 fh screw
U	2	$\frac{1}{2}$" No. 6 rh screw

*Approximate dimension; trim to fit.

THE FOUR LEGS store neatly on the bottom of the toolbox. They're held by Velco strips at one end and a retainer strap at the other.

AN OPTIONAL canvas dustcover protects tools from sawdust and dirt. A steel weight sewn in the hem holds the cover in position.

length box will accommodate. As a sawhorse, it stands at a comfortable working height of 25 in. For a lower working height, simply cut shorter legs. To obtain a higher sawhorse, you'll have to make the toolbox longer to store the legs.

The drawing also shows plans for making an optional canvas dust cover. When not in use, roll up the cover and tuck it into the box.

Cutting procedure

Study the technical drawing and materials list carefully before starting. This project requires cutting several compound angles.

Start by crosscutting a 12-in.-wide piece of ¾-in. ash-veneer plywood. Next, recut this piece to 10¾ in. wide on a table saw with the blade set at 11°. Then, lay out and cut the triangular-shaped end pieces from this board using a portable circular saw. Cut the ends slightly oversized to allow for trimming to the precise angles on the table saw.

Now, with the table saw blade set at 4° and the miter gauge set at 21°, cut one edge of each end piece. Be sure to hold the wider, bottom edge of the ends against the miter gauge. Orient the 4° bevel so that the inside face of the end is slightly *wider* than the outside surface. Turn the piece over, inside surface up, and cut the other edge. Change to a ¼-in.-wide dado blade set to 11° and cut a ¼-in.-deep dado on the inside face of each end piece. These dadoes hold the toolbox bottom.

Next, make the four legs 2 in. longer than needed. The angled leg ends will be cut later. Lay out the two ¾-in. plywood spacers that are sandwiched between the toolbox ends and the ¼-in. plywood leg guides. These triangular-shaped spacers form a channel for the legs. Cut the spacers using the miter gauge set at 21°, but adjust the saw blade to a perpendicular position and cut the edges square. Then, screw one spacer to the inside face of each end.

Note that the top 2 in. of each spacer is beveled about 7°. This allows tightening the leg clamping bolts to prevent the legs from slipping out when the sawhorse is lifted. To make these beveled cuts, first clamp or screw an 8-in.-wide auxiliary plywood fence to the table saw fence to help stabilize the workpiece and prevent tipping. Next,

position the fence so that the blade removes about ¼ in. of the spacers' thickness, and make the two cuts.

Now, set the saw blade to 21° and rip the toolbox sides from ½-in. plywood. Readjust the saw blade to 4° and use the miter gauge set at 11° to cross-cut the sides. Next, reverse the 11° angle on the miter gauge and move the gauge to the other side of the saw blade. Crosscut the other end of both sides.

Use a ¼-in.-wide dado blade tilted 21° to groove the side pieces for accepting the toolbox bottom. These grooves must align with the dadoes cut earlier in the end pieces. Now, tilt the dado blade 4°, set the miter gauge to 11° and dado the side pieces at each end to accept the ¼-in. plywood leg guides.

Cut a ¾ x ¾-in. notch in the top of each end piece for installing the handle. Then, cut the ¼-in. plywood toolbox bottom. Notch the bottom's four corners to allow the legs to pass through. Next, temporarily assemble the toolbox and mark the screw-hole locations in the sides. Also, mark the end pieces for boring ½-in.-dia. dowel holes opposite each screw. The ½-in.-dia. x ¹¹⁄₁₆-in. dowels are glued into the ends to provide solid wood for driving in screws.

Next, cut the two ¼-in. plywood leg guides which screw to the spacers. Prepare for final assembly by finish-sanding all parts.

Screw and glue a side to one end. Then, add the bottom and the second end. Position the leg guides in the dadoes and screw the second side in place. Screw the leg guides to the spacers. Next, bore a ³⁄₁₆-in.-dia. hole for the leg clamping bolt through each end, spacer and leg guide. Now, cut the handle and mount it to the toolbox.

Crosscut the hardwood legs with the saw blade set at 11° and the miter gauge set to 21°. Cut one end of all legs, then move the miter gauge to the other side of the saw blade and cut the remaining ends. Now, glue Velcro fastener strips to the inside surface of each leg and to the underside of the toolbox bottom. Be sure that the Velcro on the toolbox aligns with the Velcro on the legs. Screw the aluminum leg retainer to the toolbox bottom to hold the leg ends that don't receive Velcro. Finally, finish the toolbox with several coats of Danish oil.

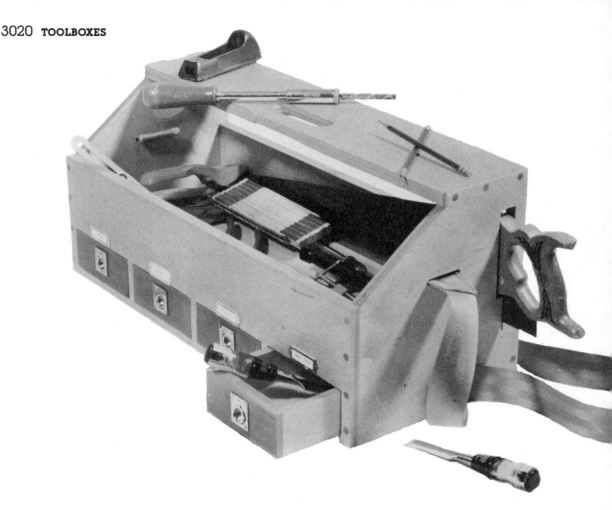

Contemporary toolbox

■ A TOOLBOX'S BASIC function is to store tools conveniently for easy job-site usage. Here is a contemporary version that appeals to today's craftsman.

Incorporated are such features as storage and on-the-job conveniences. The toolbox includes these features:

● A work surface you can use for assembly and sawing, and other carpentry operations.

● Safe storage for your prized 26-in. handsaw.

● A retractable bench stop for planing or sanding wood.

● A helpful shoulder strap that takes some of the weight off your arms when carrying the box from one job to the next.

● Four drawers for the storage of small tools and materials.

● A V-notch in the bench stop which lets it double as a "vise" of sorts. This is handy when you have to cut dowels or pipes on the jobsite.

● A bonus is the fact that the top shelf can double as a short stepladder.

For looks, we built the box of many-layered Baltic Birch plywood (though solid-core plywood could be used). Baltic Birch's multilayers provide an attractive finish and no edge work is required beyond the final sanding with 120-grit sandpaper.

How to build the box

1. Start by cutting the individual pieces to size. Use a sabre saw to cut out the drawer holes, being extremely careful to make the cuts straight and square.

2. Next, cut the rabbet and dado grooves as shown in the drawing. Temporarily assemble all parts without glue to check their fit. Mark any pieces that need refitting. Disassemble and reshape as needed.

MATERIALS LIST—TOOLBOX

Key	No.	Size and description (use)
A	1	¾ × 5½ × 25¼" Baltic Birch plywood (top)
B	2	¾ × 11 × 12" Baltic Birch plywood (sides)
C	1	¾ × 7½ × 24½" Baltic Birch plywood (back)
D	2	¾ × ¾ × 24½" pine (saw-retaining guides)
E	1	¼ × 10 × 25" hardboard (shelf)
F	1	¼ × 10 × 25" hardboard (bottom)
G	1	¾ × 4 × 4" Baltic Birch plywood (bench stop)
H	1	¾ × 7½ × 26" Baltic Birch plywood (front)
I	4	⅛ × ¾ × 8½" hardwood (drawer guides)
J	18	No. 8 × 2" fh screws
K	18	⅜" wood plugs
L	8	½ × 2⅜ × 10" plywood (drawer sides)
M	4	½ × 2⅜ × 5⅛" plywood (drawer backs)
N	4	¾ × 2⅜ × 5⅝" hardwood (drawer fronts)
O	4	Merit flush-ring pulls, Model No. 11510-3
P	4	¼ × 5⅛ × 9½" plywood (drawer bottoms)
Q	1	2" × length to suit, nylon webbing
R	2	⅜-dia. × 2" dowels
S	2	¼ × 2" carriage bolts with wingnuts and washers

Misc.: White glue, 4d finishing nails, 4 bullet catches, 4 recessed finger pulls, urethane finish.

RETRACTABLE BLOCK is raised with apex of V flush with top surface when you work a round piece.

3. To assemble, glue the false bottom and top into the sidepieces and backpiece; omit the front piece at this time.

4. Cut the ⅛x¾-in. center drawer guides from hardwood stock. Mark the center of each drawer opening and, using a square and pencil, mark the center-guide strip locations. Glue them in place.

5. Assemble the drawers with nails and glue. Test drawers for fit before the glue dries; leave the drawers in place overnight.

6. Using clamps to hold all pieces together temporarily, assemble remaining pieces with glue, screws.

7. Install the four drawers. Cut a ⅛x¾-in. notch in the bottom back edge of each drawer to straddle its center guide strip.

8. Finish with satin-finish varnish.

STOP IS adjusted up or down by loosening a pair of wingnuts.

PLANING or sanding wood is easy with the stop at one end of "workbench."

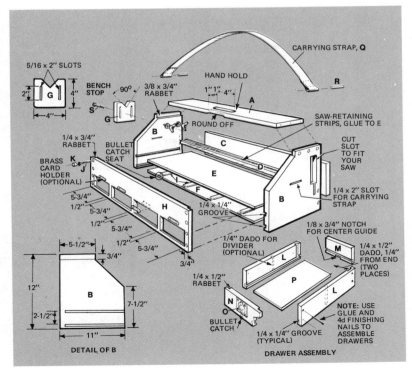

Towing secrets with a compact car

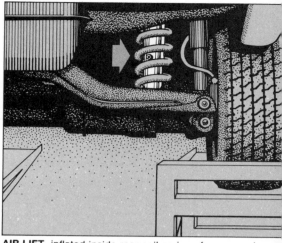

AIR LIFT, inflated inside rear coil spring of a compact car, helps to prevent sagging.

■ TROUBLE-FREE TOWING is easy when you understand the rules. New options and accessories, coupled with safe driving habits, can make the difference between safe and scary trailering with a compact car.

Match tow load to driving conditions

Match of tow load to car and driving conditions comes first. It should be figured out before you buy your rig, and must be more exact with a compact car than ever before.

The weight a compact can handle is determined by size, power and type of car, plus the routes you will drive. It is also estimated by the manufacturer, and you'd better find out what is allowed before you void your warranty.

So, go by the book. Refer to the owner's manual, and check with the manufacturer if you don't think the manual gives you the answers. You need to work out those details before you buy the car, take delivery and hitch up.

Though your car dealer and manufacturer aren't likely to admit it, a certain amount of safety factor is usually figured into their rules for towing. But the smaller the car, the more critical the limits can be. You can possibly get away with occasional overloading, but the days of casually hooking up a trailer to a makeshift bumper hitch disappeared with the arrival of smaller cars and engines.

EVEN A STERNDRIVE cruiser—nearly two tons with trailer—can be towed by a four-wheel drive car.

Type of driving

The type of driving you do and the routes you follow are going to be important. Frequent hauling of a heavy trailer at maximum speeds over hills and deserts to a steep launching ramp can strain your compact, overheat it and possibly wreck it. Offroad running across rugged terrain may punch away at springs and shocks. Lugging up steep slopes and spinning wheels in sandy spots could cook your engine and transmission oil and put added burdens on drivetrain and brakes. Bucking whipsaw gusts from passing trucks and pushing through strong winds can make steering difficult and dangerous with a heavyweight in tow.

Hitting the road for an occasional easy run over flat roads to a level campsite or launching hoist is a different towing matter.

Car maker's tow package

A car maker's "tow package" used to be a possible option. Now it should be considered essential, if available. Ask before buying the car. Not many RPO's (regular production options) can be added later without considerable difficulty and expense.

If you have a choice, consider a large engine, a high engine-to-wheel axle ratio, automatic transmission, heavy-duty suspension and radiator, power brakes and steering, heavy-duty battery and generator, equalizing hitch and platform mount and a trailer-wiring harness. You might also think about how much time you'll spend on the road and opt for tinted glass, cruise control, luggage rack, dash instruments, tilting steering wheel, reclining seats, spotlights and high-intensity running lights, airconditioner, CB radio and the rest.

With trailer in tow, you may find driving much easier and more comfortable at lower (and more economical) speeds. That will make trips longer, and you're likely to appreciate how much less tiring it is, for example, to drive with closed windows shutting out traffic noise and wind buffeting as you can with airconditioning.

Your transmission will often heat up during heavy driving with trailer in tow. An extra radiator to cool it is not usually a predelivery option, but is an important aftermarket item to consider. It can be installed by your dealer, at a garage or at home if you're a good mechanic. Side mirrors and other trailer accessories are easy do-it-yourself installations. Only the attachment of hydraulic trailer brakes cut into your car's brakes should be left to the experts.

Balance the ride

Balance and a level ride is particularly important for your smaller car. Weight on the rear of a light car tends to lift the front wheels, endangering steering control for any vehicle and reducing traction for front-wheel drive models. Choice of the proper load-balancing hitch, plus rear spring booster or air shocks will help. Supplies and luggage stored in the back of the car and in the boat or trailer behind can also ruin the level balance and cause a rear sag.

Tongue weight on the hitch ball should be 10 percent of trailer load, and total weight of loaded car and trailer should be checked on a truck-loading scale. Luggage, passengers and gear in the car and trailer can make the total weight soar. Never level an overloaded trailer by moving gear back in the trailer to lighten the tongue weight—this is dangerous.

Equalizing hitch

The equalizing hitch is engineered to lever weight forward through the chassis and distribute the trailer load to the front as well as the rear wheels. Trailers of any weight can use it, and those of 2,000 pounds and up (Class II and above) should always use it. Sway bars can be added to help reduce fishtailing.

Trailer brakes

Trailer brakes are essential for small-car towing of larger rigs, and some compacts require their use. Surge brakes are the simplest; they automatically slow the trailer as the car decelerates. Electric brakes fitted to a trailer allow control by you as you drive.

Acceleration with a small car is going to be slower and passing will be trickier, but using a small car to tow a lightweight trailer or boat need not cramp your style.

ONCE LIFTED and bolted into place, the load-distributing arms of the equalizing hitch level the load to both the front and back wheels.

IN ADDITION to the load-leveling of the hitch, sway bars secured below the trailer tongue will prevent the rig from fishtailing excessively.

A SMALL CAR towing a light aluminum boat needs a Class I hitch (under 2,000 pounds).

COMPACT'S cargo capacity can expand with this trailer.

USE OF TRUCK scales is the only accurate way to figure the weight of the car, rig and gear.

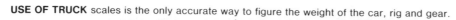

Trailer your boat

■ THE KEYS to successful longhaul boat trailering are planning, preparation, proper equipment and a few simple driving rules.

First, know for sure how much weight you're going to be towing by adding the weight of the trailer, the boat and all conceivable gear, then tacking on an ample safety margin. Second, be positive your tire capacity is sufficient for your load.

Most neophyte boat buyers start out with two strikes against them in trailering. Handicapped by inexperience, lack of knowledge and, sometimes, by an over-enthusiastic marine salesman, they break the cardinal rule of trailering by purchasing a trailer which lacks the capacity to carry anything more than the bare boat. Forgotten are the life preservers, anchor, fuel tanks, fuel, fishing gear, water skis, first-aid kit, canvas top and boat cover, plus that mass of paraphernalia required by the modern camping family.

The capacity of a trailer depends on its structural design, materials, assembly, coupler, axle, springs, hubs, bearings, wheels and tires. It's a complicated engineering equation, so for the most part, the average trailer buyer has to rely on the manufacturer's capacity rating. However, the most likely candidate for weak-link-in-the-chain is tire capacity.

PROTECTIVE DEVICES which keep water out of the trailer hubs let you submerge wheels without wetting bearings.

The message here is twofold. First, know for sure how much weight you're going to be towing by adding the weight of the trailer, the boat and all conceivable gear, then tacking on an ample safety margin. Second, be positive your tire capacity is sufficient for your load.

You can increase tire capacity by using larger tires or switching to a tandem trailer which has four wheels. Generally, though, it's better to stay with a two-wheel trailer until you're forced to use a tandem. One high-capacity tire is a 7x10.5 tube-type tire designed for use on mobile homes, which has a 2000-pound rating.

Long-distance hauling

For long-distance hauling with a boat over 16 ft. long, use automotive-sized wheels and tires. The advantages are many: increased load capacity, greater traction, longer tire life, better road handling, greater clearance, longer wheelbearing life and easier handling. When practical, it's advantageous to have similar wheels on trailer and towing vehicle.

Tire inflation should be maintained at pressures recommended by the tire manufacturer. Under-inflated boat trailer tires will cause accelerated and uneven tread wear, sway (especially at high speeds) and excessive internal heat.

The most common cause of trailer failure is bearing failure—one problem that's easy to avoid. Few novice trailer boaters are aware of the potential trouble resulting from submerging trailer wheel hubs while launching and retrieving their craft.

Bearing failure

When bearings become wet—usually from submersion, but also from condensation—they corrode. This causes excessive friction between the bearings and the bearing race, and the resulting heat melts the protective grease inside the hub. As long as the bearings are smooth, the temperature of bearing grease is about equal to the traveling speed plus the air temperature. That is, at 55 mph on an 85° day the grease temperature would be approximately 140° F. High-quality greases will not melt and lose their effectiveness until the internal hub temperature climbs to 300° F. Around 1500° or 1600°, plastic deformation occurs and metal softens to a buttery consistency. At 2500° to 3000° the bearings melt and then fuse to the axle.

It's no fun when you are driving happily toward your launching site and suddenly hear the screech of a bearing which has collapsed for just this reason.

The obvious solution is never to submerge the wheel hubs while launching. However, this is impossible on the majority of back-country ramps and, depending upon the boat design and trailer construction, may even be impossible on an ultra-modern ramp.

Three ways to protect bearings

There are three basic protective devices designed to keep water from the bearings. They may be classed generally as grease under injection pressure, inflation under pressure and oil bath. We've used them all and, while not completely fail-safe, they all work. Fortunately for boaters, these devices have recently become standard or optional equipment with most major trailer manufacturers.

With the grease system, you fill the hub with grease through a device which replaces the dust cap. A piston creates a slight pressure inside the hub, and there's a pressure-relief device to prevent rupture of any seals. With the hub full of grease under controlled pressure, water cannot enter.

The air-pressure system utilizes air under pressure to do the same thing. The hub is sealed off and, prior to each submersion, air is pumped into the cavity through an air valve, using a hand bulb pump.

The oil-bath system maintains a reservoir of oil within the hub cavity to insure that bearings will remain water-free and constantly lubricated. The dust cap is replaced with a transparent cover which has a filler plug for oil replacement. The level is easily checked by visual examination.

We can't recommend any one system as the best, but we strongly urge every trailer boater to install one of these devices and keep it properly maintained.

It's impossible to emphasize too strongly the importance of good trailer brakes, especially if most of your experience has been in short-haul, flatland trailering. For the light rig, of course, they're not necessary.

There's no specific point where brakes are definitely required, since many factors are involved in the ability to stop. The most important of these are the braking capacity of the vehicle, weight of the tow load, extent of grade, speed and road surface conditions. However, when the gross weight of a two-wheeled trailer approaches 3000 pounds, or exceeds 3500 pounds with any tandem trailer, brakes are not a luxury but a life-saving necessity. One major automobile company even recommends brakes for any trailer weighing more than 1200 pounds.

Electric or hydraulic brakes

Most auto manufacturers state that electric brakes are far superior to hydraulic brakes, whether operated by an activator on the trailer coupler ("surge" brakes) or connected directly to the vehicle's hydraulic brake line. The one danger of the direct connection is the possibility of losing all braking power through a malfunction in the trailer's vulnerable external system.

Most electric brakes used today operate automatically when the car's brake pedal is depressed. If desired, the trailer brakes may be applied manually by moving a small lever similar to a turn-signal control. A simple adjustment at the activator switch adjusts the brakes for varying loads. The trailer brakes are applied just before the vehicle brakes make contact, thus preventing the boat from pushing the vehicle forward. This keeps the entire rig on a true course while slowing down.

State laws requiring brakes on boat trailers vary, so check your state's regulations for the exact legal requirements.

Your towing vehicle

As for towing power, you just can't beat a husky pickup camper. Automobiles, station wagons, vans and even a VW sedan all had one common failing—they just weren't designed to go ranging about the countryside with a 3000 to 6000-pound load behind.

The inherent advantages of a pickup are obvious—heavier springs, greater stability, better cooling ability, low ratio axle and better braking. Even with trucks, however, you have to buy one that will match your towing weight requirements. Of course, manufacturers offer optional equipment for both pickups and automobiles to make towing safer and easier. Among the options are higher-capacity cooling systems, four-speed or automatic transmissions, lower axle ratios, anti-spin differentials, larger springs, power brakes, extra-capacity batteries and alternators, flotation tires and dual trailering mirrors.

Boat towing means slow going

Boat towing generally means slow going, but you can make good time with a camper, because of fewer and shorter stops. Meals are quick and easy with the conveniences of a gas range, refrigerator (not an icebox), hot and cold running water, and even a toilet and shower, if you like. You can roll past motel no-vacancy signs without a worry, because your bedroom's right behind you.

At overnight stops the boat's lounge seats and canvas top give a spare bedroom where the youngsters can be bedded down while the camper is still in use. On the road, the boat functions as a luggage trailer which keeps the camper uncluttered. It's perfect for carrying bulky, light objects, such as a couple of comfortable aluminum chaise lounges for predinner relaxation.

Plan for a high-mileage day

If you want to get a high-mileage day, let the children continue sleeping in the camper in the morning and drive for two or three hours before stopping to roll up the sleeping bags and prepare the bacon and eggs. Perhaps you can fix sandwiches to save time at noon. In any case, you can always prepare mid-afternoon snacks during this morning stop.

Costs kept down

Once you have the equipment, a camping-boating vacation is surprisingly easy on the budget. Your principal expenses for boat-camping, other than for groceries, are limited to gasoline and minimal campground fees.

Driving techniques

Driving techniques on a long trip are similar to other towing situations. The main rule is to allow plenty of time so you won't feel a need to hurry. Avoid driving at night. Plan to arrive at your stop with ample time to park the vehicle and get set before dark.

On the road, allow ample distance to stop smoothly and gradually. Let faster drivers have the right of way. You'll find that just plain courtesy pays off. When climbing a grade, use low gears to avoid overheating. Always use the lower gears on down grades of any length or steepness. It's much better to creep down a grade at 25 mph in second gear than to try to save a few minutes by staying in third gear and have to ride the brake pedal all the way.

If you have to drive over a bumpy, unpaved road with your boat, drive extremely slowly (10-15 mph). Boats are designed for water-cushioned bumps and trailers for smooth highways. Both take an unmerciful beating on rutty roads.

Launching tips

The main thing to watch for in launching your boat on a wilderness ramp is to be positive there's a firm footing for your rear tires and that there's enough water depth to handle the boat. Always carry a tow rope, so if necessary, you can unhook the trailer from the camper and push it farther into the water. The same works in reverse. You can push the trailer into the water for loading the boat and then pull the trailer back to firm ground with the tow cable where you can hitch it to the vehicle. Tandem wheels or flotation tires are worthwhile, if you use non-paved ramps with soft footing regularly.

The boat hull or engine installation may dictate the type of hull support. If there's a choice, we favor a roller system over straight padded cradles for easier launching operations and to keep wheel hubs out of the water.

The right kind of hitch

A frame-mounted hitch generally is completely adequate on pickup trucks, but with an automobile most manufacturers recommend using a load-equalizing hitch for loads over 2000 pounds and a tongue weight over 200 pounds. This type hitch redistributes the tongue load in such a way as to prevent all of the load from resting on the ball hitch. Some of the weight is transferred to the front wheels of the towing vehicle and some is shifted back to the trailer wheels. The size of hitch and torsion bars used must match the load.

The above rundown on towing weights, size of tires and other technical features may seem mighty complicated. Actually, it reduces to a very small checklist which is a real headache eliminator.

When it comes to outdoor vacation fun for the entire family, nothing equals the enjoyment of hitting the road in a camper with a boat trailering merrily behind.

Blockmobile fleet

■ A FLEET of these classy blockmobiles will provide hours of fun for a 4-year-old, and they can be made for practically nothing from scraps of ¾ and 1½-in. pine found in your woodbox. They are also practically unbreakable.

All are made by first gluing up blocks of varying thicknesses after precutting them to shape. All fender "wells" are bored ½ in. deep with a 1⅜-in. spade power bit. Then $\frac{5}{16}$-in. holes are drilled from each side for free-turning axles of ¼-in. dowel rod.

The wheels are easy to make if you own a lathe, but there are other ways to make them. One way is with a hole cutter in a drill press; another is with a pivot jig clamped to the table of a disc sander. In a pinch, checkers could be used for wheels.

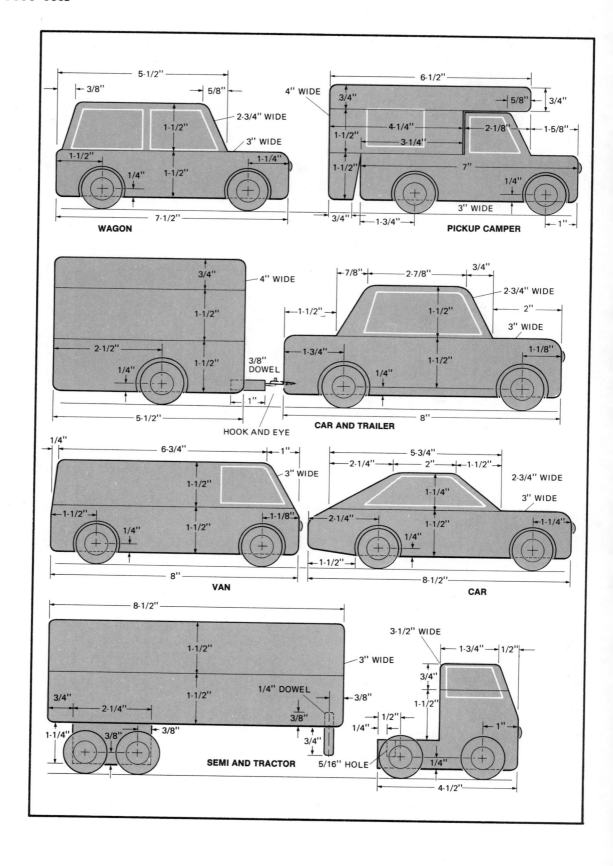

WAGON

PICKUP CAMPER

CAR AND TRAILER

HOOK AND EYE

3/8" DOWEL

VAN

CAR

SEMI AND TRACTOR

5/16" HOLE

1/4" DOWEL

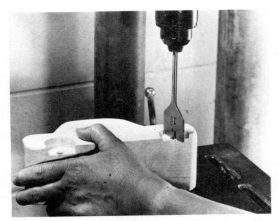

FENDER WELLS for wheels are made ½ in. deep with 1⅜-in. spade-type bit chucked in drill press.

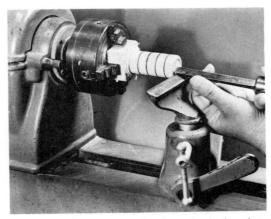

WHEELS are turned one at a time from chucked turning. Shape hub and tire first, then cut it off.

GLUE WHEELS to axles after inserting axles in their holes and slipping washers over the ends.

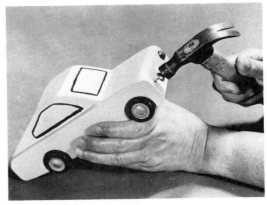

FANCY-HEAD upholstery nails make perfect headlights. Wooden screw-hole buttons, painted, can also be used.

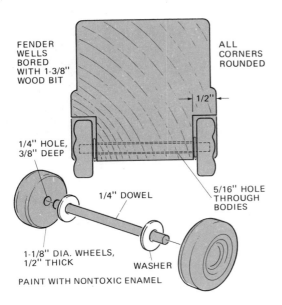

FENDER WELLS BORED WITH 1-3/8" WOOD BIT

ALL CORNERS ROUNDED

1/2"

1/4" HOLE, 3/8" DEEP

5/16" HOLE THROUGH BODIES

1/4" DOWEL

1-1/8" DIA. WHEELS, 1/2" THICK

WASHER

PAINT WITH NONTOXIC ENAMEL

The best way to turn the wheels is to gang-turn them from a single turning as shown in the photo above. Here the wheels are cut off one by one after you form a hub on the face of the wheels and round the edges to form a tire. The wheels are glued onto the ends of the dowel axles after being drilled ⅜ in. deep from the inside. Washers keep the wheels from rubbing and sticking. It's best to paint the wheels beforehand.

It's important, of course, to round all sharp edges, sand the wood smooth and paint the vehicles with a *nontoxic* paint.

Upholstery tacks are used for headlights, and a small L-hook and screw eye are used as a hitch for the car and trailer.

Buzzing bumblebee

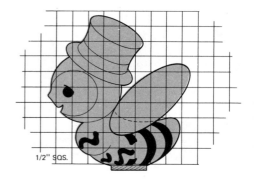

1/2" SQS.

■ AS THIS TOY is pulled along by a youngster, the smiling bee "buzzes" around the petal continuously, "alighting" only when the pulling stops. While sure to delight toddlers, this pull toy will make parents happy as well because the "buzzing" is silent.

As can be seen in the drawing at left, the toy is far easier to make than one would suppose when watching the finished toy in action. Parts are easy to make and assemble; no sophisticated tools, techniques or knowledge are called for in the making. In fact, the project can be completed entirely with handtools using a coping saw for shaping petals and bee, brace and bit for all necessary boring. The rest of the job calls for gluing, sawing, nailing and finish-painting with nontoxic paint.

The wheels on the toy shown were cut from 1/2-in.-thick plywood. If you lack a jigsaw or holesaw—either of which must be used to cut perfect circles—buy a length of 2-in.-dia. hardwood dowel, and cut off 1/2-in.-thick pieces like slices of bologna.

It is best to tack-assemble the toy before finishing to assure that moving parts work as they should. When satisfied, disassemble the piece, do the finish painting and permanently assemble.

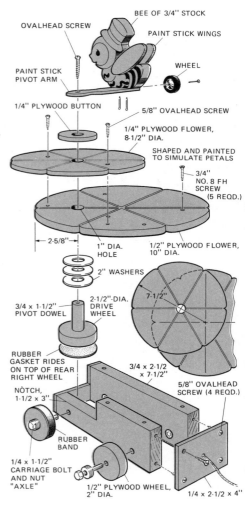

OVALHEAD SCREW

BEE OF 3/4" STOCK

PAINT STICK WINGS

PAINT STICK PIVOT ARM

WHEEL

1/4" PLYWOOD BUTTON

5/8" OVALHEAD SCREW

1/4" PLYWOOD FLOWER, 8-1/2" DIA.

SHAPED AND PAINTED TO SIMULATE PETALS

3/4" NO. 8 FH SCREW (5 REQD.)

2-5/8"

1" DIA. HOLE

1/2" PLYWOOD FLOWER, 10" DIA.

7-1/2"

2" WASHERS

3/4 x 1-1/2" PIVOT DOWEL

2-1/2"-DIA. DRIVE WHEEL

3/4 x 2-1/2 x 7-1/2"

5/8" OVALHEAD SCREW (4 REQD.)

RUBBER GASKET RIDES ON TOP OF REAR RIGHT WHEEL

NOTCH, 1-1/2 x 3"

RUBBER BAND

1/4 x 1-1/2" CARRIAGE BOLT AND NUT "AXLE"

1/2" PLYWOOD WHEEL, 2" DIA.

1/4 x 2-1/2 x 4"

UPSIDE-DOWN view shows what makes the bee buzz—rubber gasket on drive wheel rides atop the rear wheel.

Ducks and dachshunds that talk

■ TODDLERS LIKE TOYS they can pull all around the house. If they also make a noise, so much the better. Here are a couple of animal pull toys you can make in your shop that are sure to please any toddler. Mom Duck and her kids waddle along quacking merrily and Danny Dachshund makes himself heard and waddles his hind quarters as he is pulled. Off-center wheels provide the waddle, and compression-spring necks make the heads bob. Both the ducks and

the dog have the same voice. It is produced by pieces of clock spring being snapped against sounding boxes by hardwood ratchets.

The photos show all of the steps necessary in making the ducks. Notice in each case that the voice-box holes are bored before the blocks are slotted and sawed out. Card stock is just right for the cardboard sounding-box discs. A dab of glue is used to hold the ratchet (clacker) on the axle and

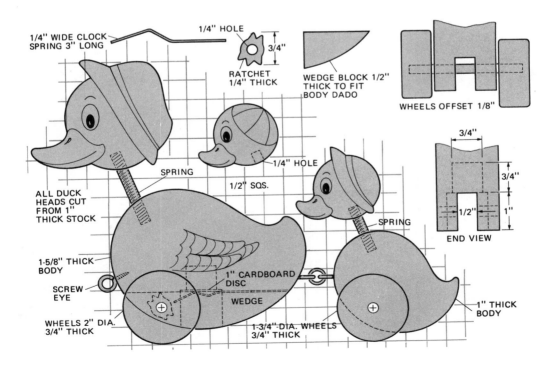

1/4" WIDE CLOCK SPRING 3" LONG

1/4" HOLE

RATCHET 1/4" THICK

3/4"

WEDGE BLOCK 1/2" THICK TO FIT BODY DADO

WHEELS OFFSET 1/8"

ALL DUCK HEADS CUT FROM 1" THICK STOCK

SPRING

1/4" HOLE

1/2" SQS.

SPRING

3/4"

3/4"

1/2"

1"

END VIEW

1-5/8" THICK BODY

SCREW EYE

1" CARDBOARD DISC

WEDGE

WHEELS 2" DIA. 3/4" THICK

1-3/4"-DIA. WHEELS 3/4" THICK

1" THICK BODY

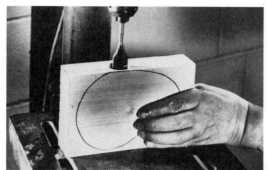

SOUNDING-BOX holes are bored in block before the body is cut out. Drill 1-in. hole first, then ¾ in.

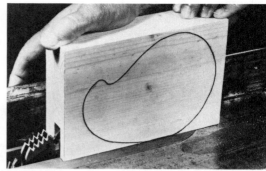

BLOCK IS passed over dado saw to form ½-inch-wide slot in bottom edge, drilled for axles then sawed.

THIN CARDBOARD disc is glued to ledge formed by large hole to cover the ¾-in. sounding-box hole.

RATCHET IS SLIPPED over axle as it's passed through slot. Glue on each side holds ratchet on axle.

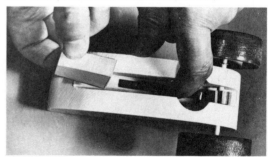

APPLY GLUE to wedge block, then insert block in slot to hold the spring against the cardboard and ratchet.

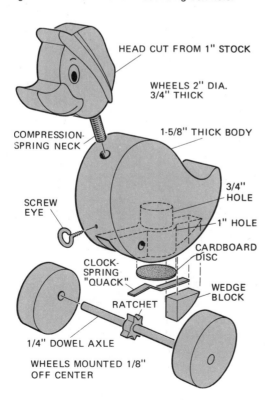

HEAD CUT FROM 1" STOCK

WHEELS 2" DIA.
3/4" THICK

COMPRESSION-
SPRING NECK

1-5/8" THICK BODY

3/4"
HOLE

1" HOLE

SCREW
EYE

CARDBOARD
DISC

CLOCK-
SPRING
"QUACK"

WEDGE
BLOCK

RATCHET

1/4" DOWEL AXLE

WHEELS MOUNTED 1/8"
OFF CENTER

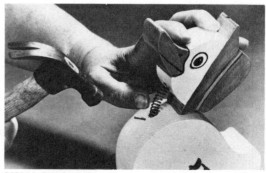

SMALL FINISHING nails, plus glue, are used to anchor neck springs in holes. Drive nails crosswise.

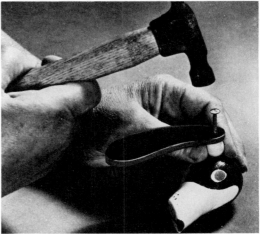

ATTACH EARS to head by driving nails through oversize holes in the ears, then through wooden beads.

ATTACH HIND quarters to front section with washer between by driving nail through oversize hole.

in the center of the slot. A wedge block is inserted in the slot to hold the spring against the cardboard. Finally small finishing nails and glue are used to anchor the neck springs.

Basically, Danny is made the same way, the exception being that only his rear wheels are placed off-center. Waddle is produced by attaching his hind quarters with a nail in an oversize hole. His head is lathe-turned and then cut off at an angle to form nose and mouth.

The wheels can be cut easily from ½-inch stock with a hole cutter for either of the toys. Finally, sand all parts smooth and then paint with a nontoxic enamel.

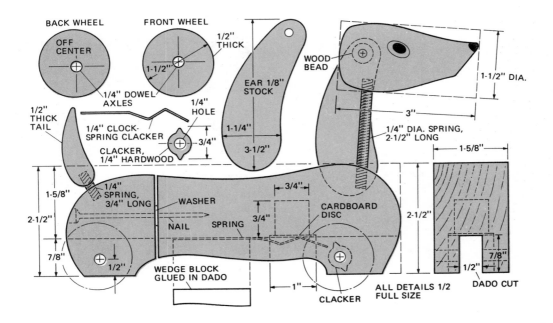

1

2

Playthings for your youngsters

■ ONE OF THE more rewarding aspects for the active home work-shopper is building things for children.

The reward is two-fold: First, you get to share the joy that is triggered by the giving of toys such as those pictured. The second is the smug satisfaction of being a "hero" (that only the builders of kids' furniture ever get to know).

On these pages we have rounded up four fun projects to keep you and your children busy.

1 PM'S CHILD-POWERED digger works beautifully—just like the real ones—and will give the user hours of fun.

2 SLEEK MODEL RACER is easy to make: body is cut from a scrap piece of 2x4. Mag wheels are created using a hole saw; the roll bar is a U-bolt.

3 HERE'S A PLAY center to wow preschoolers (and older youngsters). It has a play TV, bulletin board, chalkboard (top), and place to make up (above).

4 DOLL CRADLE is reproduction of 18th-century cradle. Ours is handcrafted of mellow pine with varnish finish.

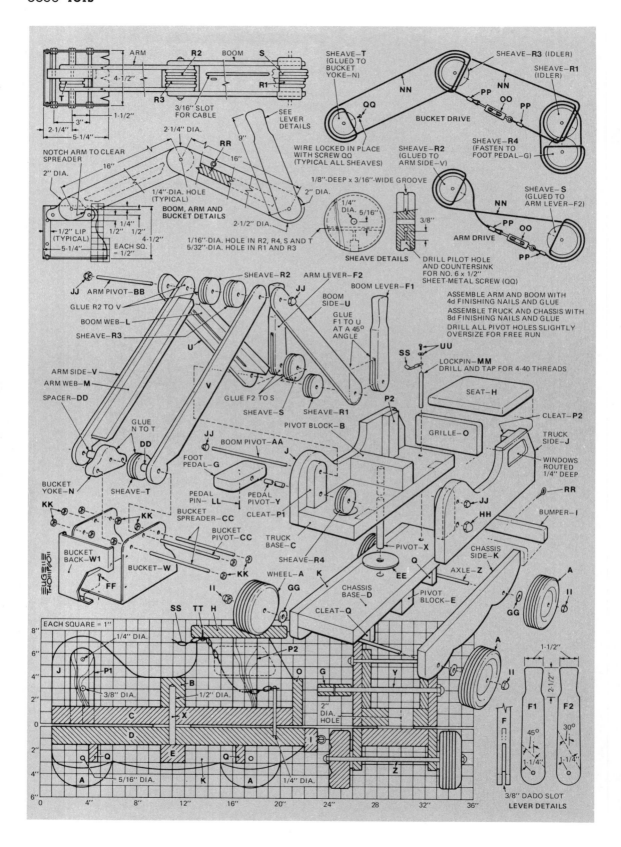

ARM

R2 BOOM S

R1

R3

4-1/2"

1-1/2"

3"

2-1/4"

5-1/4"

3/16" SLOT FOR CABLE

SEE LEVER DETAILS

T

SHEAVE–T (GLUED TO BUCKET YOKE–N)

NN

QQ

SHEAVE–R3 (IDLER)

SHEAVE–R1 (IDLER)

NN

OO

PP

PP

BUCKET DRIVE

2-1/4" DIA.

RR

NOTCH ARM TO CLEAR SPREADER

2" DIA.

16"

9"

16"

2" DIA.

WIRE LOCKED IN PLACE WITH SCREW QQ (TYPICAL ALL SHEAVES)

SHEAVE–R2 (GLUED TO ARM SIDE–V)

SHEAVE–R4 (FASTEN TO FOOT PEDAL–G)

1/4"-DIA. HOLE (TYPICAL)

BOOM, ARM AND BUCKET DETAILS

2-1/2" DIA.

1/8"-DEEP x 3/16"-WIDE GROOVE

SHEAVE–S (GLUED TO ARM LEVER–F2)

NN

1/4" DIA. 5/16"

3/8"

ARM DRIVE

OO

PP

PP

1/2" LIP (TYPICAL)

1/4" 1/2" 1/2"

4-1/2"

5-1/4"

EACH SQ. = 1/2"

1/16"-DIA. HOLE IN R2, R4, S AND T
5/32"-DIA. HOLE IN R1 AND R3

SHEAVE DETAILS

DRILL PILOT HOLE AND COUNTERSINK FOR NO. 6 x 1/2" SHEET-METAL SCREW (QQ)

JJ

ARM PIVOT–BB

GLUE R2 TO V

BOOM WEB–L

SHEAVE–R3

SHEAVE–R2

ARM LEVER–F2

JJ

BOOM SIDE–U

BOOM LEVER–F1

ASSEMBLE ARM AND BOOM WITH 4d FINISHING NAILS AND GLUE

ASSEMBLE TRUCK AND CHASSIS WITH 8d FINISHING NAILS AND GLUE

DRILL ALL PIVOT HOLES SLIGHTLY OVERSIZE FOR FREE RUN

GLUE F1 TO U AT A 45° ANGLE

SS

UU

LOCKPIN–MM

DRILL AND TAP FOR 4-40 THREADS

ARM SIDE–V

ARM WEB–M

SPACER–DD

U

V

GLUE F2 TO S

SHEAVE–S

SHEAVE–R1

SEAT–H

CLEAT–P2

GLUE N TO T

DD

JJ

BOOM PIVOT–AA

J

P2

PIVOT BLOCK–B

GRILLE–O

TRUCK SIDE–J

WINDOWS ROUTED 1/4" DEEP

BUCKET YOKE–N

SHEAVE–T

FOOT PEDAL–G

PEDAL PIN–LL

PEDAL PIVOT–Y

CLEAT–P1

JJ

HH

RR

BUMPER–I

KK

KK

KK

BUCKET SPREADER–CC

BUCKET PIVOT–CC

TRUCK BASE–C

SHEAVE–R4

K

PIVOT–X

EE

Q

CHASSIS SIDE–K

AXLE–Z

A

II

BUCKET BACK–W1

BUCKET–W

FF

KK

WHEEL–A

GG

CHASSIS BASE–D

CLEAT–Q

PIVOT BLOCK–E

GG

EUGENE THOMPSON

II

SS TT H

EACH SQUARE = 1"

8"

6"

4"

2"

0

2"

4"

6"

1/4" DIA.

P2

J

P1

3/8" DIA.

B

1/2" DIA.

C

X

D

E

Q

K

A

5/16" DIA.

Q

A

1/4" DIA.

O G

G

Y

2" DIA. HOLE

I

Z

A

II

A

GG

II

1-1/2"

2-1/2"

F1 F2

45°

30°

1-1/4"

1-1/4"

F

3/8" DADO SLOT

LEVER DETAILS

0 4" 8" 12" 16" 20" 24" 28" 32" 36"

CHILD-POWERED DIGGER

This is an ideal project for the craftsman who wants to build an exceptional toy for a youngster. The digger works beautifully and provides hours of fun and exercise for its proud young owner.

Using a cable and sheave mechanism, the arm and boom are precisely operated with hand levers, while the attitude of the bucket for loading and dumping is controlled with a foot pedal. The young operator uses both hands and feet to operate the machine, which works fine in sand, sawdust, or snow.

Making the sheaves

Start by making the boom mechanism and sheaves. Lay out and cut the six pulleys and sheaves from ¾-in.-thick hardwood with a band saw. One easy way to mount the stock in the lathe for turning is to bore a ¼-in. center hole in each blank and use a ¼-20 machine screw turned into your tapered screw center after removing the existing screw. Turn the outside diameter of the sheave blank true, then turn a groove ³/₁₆-in. wide by ⅛-in. deep for the cable. Round-over both edges of the sheave. Smooth up the face, leaving the center slightly thicker than the edges for clearance. Sand and finish with varnish, then remove the stock from the lathe.

Enlarge the center hole on all sheaves to achieve a running fit on the ¼-in. axles. To do it, use a ⁹/₃₂-in. bit. Watching the bank of sheaves turning is part of the enjoyment that the young operator derives from using this toy.

CABLE GROOVE in sheave is turned so it will accommodate two turns of cable.

THROUGH-HOLES in sheaves are bored parallel to diameter.

BOOM AND ARM are assembled with axles and sheaves in place temporarily.

RECESSES ARE routed in truck sides to simulate windows.

TRUCK is for outdoors so assemble with waterproof glue, finishing nails.

TIRE FACES and treads are turned on lathe; note dead center support.

ALUMINUM parts for the bucket were formed on small bending brake.

BUCKET PIVOTS on end of arm; spacers on rod keep bucket centered.

SHEAVE rotational positions and attitude relationship are critical.

Bore holes through the sheaves from groove to groove parallel with the diameter, *but offset slightly to miss the axle holes.* These holes should be $1/16$ in. in the small and one of the medium sheaves, and $5/32$ in. in the large and three of the medium sheaves. Bore the holes *across the grain* for strength. Drill and countersink for sheet-metal screws at right angles to the cable holes for locking the cable in the sheave where needed.

The boom arm

Cut the boom pieces from the $3/8$-in. exterior plywood as shown. Tack the pieces together in groups of two. On your jointer (or with a hand plane) make an overall $1/4$-in. taper on the width of both stacks. Lay out the $1/4$-in. holes, spaced 16 in. on center. Scribe the rounded ends with a compass, then cut and sand the rounded ends of the stacks. Bore the $1/4$-in. axle holes, then disassemble the stacks and round all edges of the boom and arm sides with a router and rounding-over bit.

Next, lay out and cut the operating handles. Cut a $3/8$-in. dado slot in both handles to fit the plywood sides of the boom. Bottoms of the dadoes must be made at appropriate angles. The boom handle is glued to the $3/8$-in. plywood at a 45° angle.

The arm-operating handle straddles the right-hand boom stringer with a 30° limit cut at the bottom of the slot.

If you are using a circular saw, clamp the handle to a scrap of plywood at the appropriate angle to kerf the slot. Round edges with a router, bore the $1/4$-in. holes and glue the handle to the boom stringer. Using waterproof glue, fasten the largest wheel to the side of the arm-operating straddle lever.

Study photos and drawings and complete gluing operations before you assemble the boom, arm and bucket. Reinforce with $1/4$-in. dowels.

Make the web for the boom and arm of 1-in. stock. Slot one web where the cables must cross, as shown. Assemble the boom and arm parts with waterproof glue and brads, with axles temporarily installed for alignment. Disassemble axles and paint boom/arm parts, then reassemble.

Making truck sides

Stack two pieces of $3/4$-in. stock and lay out, band saw and bore holes as shown on diagram. Round all edges with a router and rounding-over bit except the sides adjoining the roof and front grille, and inside the bottom edge. Rout $1/4$-in.-deep recesses to simulate cab windows.

Assemble strengthening cleats to the bottom and sides, using waterproof glue and nails. Assemble in the same way the blocks for the pivot rod through the base and vertical cleats inside the truck sides at trunnion and cab. Rebore the $1/2$-in. hole for the body pivot not quite through the block.

From $3/4$-in. stock, cut out the grille, front bumper, two chassis skirts, two skirt spreaders and foot pedal. The seat should be of 1-in. hardwood with the grain running across the truck. Round all corners and edges where appropriate, and assemble parts with waterproof glue and finishing nails. Imitation lights and grille ornaments were added on the prototype.

MATERIALS LIST—CHILD-POWERED DIGGER

Key	No.	Size and description (use)
A	4	$1\frac{3}{4} \times 5$"-dia. hardwood (wheels)
B	1	$2 \times 2\frac{1}{2} \times 5\frac{1}{2}$" hardwood (pivot block)
C	1	$1\frac{1}{2} \times 5\frac{1}{2} \times 20$" hardwood (truck base)
D	1	$1\frac{1}{2} \times 5\frac{1}{2} \times 21$" hardwood (chassis base)
E	1	$1\frac{1}{2} \times 2 \times 5\frac{1}{2}$" hardwood (chassis pivot block)
F1	1	$1 \times 2 \times 10$" hardwood (boom lever)
F2	1	$1 \times 2 \times 10$" hardwood (arm lever)
G	1	$1 \times 2\frac{3}{4} \times 5$" hardwood (foot pedal)
H	1	$1 \times 7\frac{1}{2} \times 8$" hardwood (seat)
I	1	$1 \times 1\frac{3}{4} \times 8$" pine or hardwood (bumper)
J	2	$3/4 \times 7\frac{1}{2} \times 20$" pine or hardwood (truck sides)
K	2	$3/4 \times 3\frac{1}{2} \times 21$" pine or hardwood (chassis sides)
L	1	$3/4 \times 2\frac{1}{4} \times 13\frac{3}{8}$" pine or hardwood (boom web)
M	1	$3/4 \times 1\frac{1}{2} \times 13\frac{1}{8}$" pine or hardwood (arm web)
N	1	$3/4 \times 2 \times 4$" hardwood (bucket yoke)
O	1	$3/4 \times 4 \times 7$" pine or hardwood (grille)
P1	2	$3/4 \times 1\frac{1}{2} \times 5$" pine (cleats)
P2	2	$3/4 \times 1\frac{1}{2} \times 6$" pine (cleats)
Q	2	$3/4 \times 2 \times 6$" pine (chassis cleats)
R	4	$3/4 \times 2\frac{1}{2}$"-dia. hardwood (sheave)
S	1	$3/4 \times 3$"-dia. hardwood (sheave)
T	1	$3/4 \times 2$"-dia. hardwood (sheave)
U	2	$3/8 \times 2\frac{1}{2} \times 18\frac{3}{8}$" plywood (boom side)
V	1	$3/8 \times 2\frac{1}{4} \times 18\frac{1}{8}$" plywood (arm side)
W	1	$3/32 \times 3\frac{1}{4} \times 13\frac{1}{2}$" aluminum (bucket)
W1	1	$3/32 \times 3\frac{1}{4} \times 5\frac{1}{2}$" aluminum (bucket back)
X	1	$1/2$"-dia. $\times 5$" steel rod (truck pivot)
Y	1	$3/8$"-dia. $\times 5$" steel rod (pedal pivot)
Z	2	$5/16$"-dia. $\times 11\frac{1}{2}$" steel rod (axles)
AA	1	$1/3$"-dia. $\times 1\frac{1}{2}$" steel rod (boom pivot)
BB	1	$1/4$"-dia. $\times 3\frac{1}{2}$" steel rod (arm pivot)
CC	3	$1/4$"-dia. $\times 5$" threaded steel rods (bucket and pivot spreaders)
DD	2	$5/16$"-i.d. $\times 1\frac{1}{16}$" metal or plastic tube (spacers)
EE	1	$1/2$"-i.d., 3"-o.d. leather washer
FF	5	$1/8$"-dia. cold rivets
GG	4	$5/16$"-i.d. flat washers
HH	1	$3/8$" pushnut
II	4	$5/16$" pushnuts
JJ	4	$1/4$" pushnuts
KK	1	$1/4$-20 hex nut
LL	1	8d finish nail cut to 1" (pedal pin)
MM	1	$1/4$"-dia. $\times 4$" steel rod (lockpin)
NN	1	$1/16$" steel airplane cable (20 ft.)
OO	2	Turnbuckles
PP	4	Double-hole swedges
QQ	1	No. 6 $\times 1/2$" sheet-metal screws
RR	2	$1/2$" screw eyes
SS	1	16" sash chain with snap hook
TT	1	No. 8 $\times 1/2$" rh screws
UU	1	4-40 $\times 1/2$" rh screws and washers

The wheels and bucket

Band saw four 5-in. blanks from 2-in. stock. For turning, glue sandpaper to a wood faceplate to act as a friction drive. Place a blank against the sandpaper and bring up the dead center to engage the compass detent at the center of the blank. Turn the tire and face of the wheel, then bore the $\frac{5}{16}$-in. axle hole. Paint the tires black, the wheels as you prefer.

Aluminum sheet $\frac{3}{32}$-in. thick is available at scrap-metal yards or duct-fabrication shops. Lay out bucket parts according to the drawing. Cutting can be done on a band saw as aluminum is softer than the woodcutting blade.

Drill $\frac{1}{4}$-in. holes for the yoke rods. Bending is done on a small brake clamped to the circular-saw table. You could do a suitable job with a machinist's vise and hammer. Make the bends and assemble the back to the bucket with cold rivets.

Assemble the bucket to the yoke with two $\frac{1}{4}$-in. rods threaded at both ends. The front rod has nuts on the inside of the bucket and on outside faces to prevent collapsing and spreading. Bucket sides at the front rod must be slightly sprung to install the front rod with internal nuts in place.

Assemble the yoke to the end of the arm with $\frac{1}{4}$-in. rod threaded at both ends, a tube spacer and washer on each side of the yoke, and nuts on the outside at rod ends. Mushroom rod ends slightly to keep nuts tight. Assemble the arm and boom with $\frac{1}{4}$-in. rod and pushnuts. Assemble the boom to trunnions on the truck with $\frac{1}{4}$-in. rod, pushnuts, washers and spacers.

Installing the foot pedal

Make the foot pedal $2\frac{3}{4}$ in. wide by 5 in. long from hardwood stock 1 in. thick. The pedal controls the attitude of the bucket. Even when boom and arm levers move, a consistent position of the pedal holds the position of the bucket. Changing the bucket attitude responds well to movement of the pedal.

Drill the pedal through its width for the $\frac{3}{8}$-in. rod that will pass through the lower part of the truck trunnions and accept the hardwood pedal on one end. Tap the rod into the pedal flush with the edge, then pin it with an 8d finishing nail in a hole drilled through pedal and rod. Looking toward the rear from the front, pass the rod through the right trunnion and slip on a $2\frac{1}{2}$-in.-dia. sheave. Pass rod end through the left trunnion and install a pushnut. Do not pin sheave to the rod until the cable is run.

Determine cable lengths by running string through and around the sheaves. Looking aft, the shorter cable on the right connects the sheave glued to the operating lever with that glued to the arm, operating the arm. The longer cable interconnects the four sheaves on the left—pinned sheave on the foot-pedal rod, two idlers at ends of the boom and small sheave glued to the bucket yoke. This controls the bucket attitude. Use string as guides to cut cable lengths.

Airplane cable of $\frac{1}{16}$-in. diameter should be found at an industrial hardware store. Pull cable loosely around the sheaves and through locking holes, and adjust sheaves by rotating them to allow proper turning leeway. Start at lowest sheaves, leaving 10 or 12 in. of cable loose for turnbuckle attachment under boom.

Tighten lockscrews (sheet-metal screws with points ground flat) at these lower sheaves before final routing of the cable. Attach cable ends to the turnbuckles with double-hole swedges (crimp-on cable clamps) appropriate for $\frac{1}{16}$-in. cable (an industrial hardware store should have them). Here, a swedging tool was made with holes drilled in a flat bar, and a hacksaw cut made through the centers of the holes.

Check and adjust sheave rotational positions for leeway in movement and cable tightness before you tighten the lockscrew on the outboard sheave. If cable holes in any sheaves are too large, insert one or two short pieces of cable in the hole. Adjust arm lever to arm position before locking it. Repeat the procedure for the bucket-control cable from foot pedal. Holes in idler sheaves must be large enough for two thicknesses of cable. Attach swedged loops to turnbuckles, tighten cables.

Finish assembly

With parts prepainted and truck-boom assembly completed, pivot the truck body to the chassis. Cut a pivot pin from $\frac{1}{2}$-in.-dia. steel rod, to a length just short of the depth of both holes plus the washer. A waxed leather disc was used on the prototype; metal discs will serve as thrust washers. A small chain anchored by a screw under the roof has an end snap hook to engage a screw eye on the boom. It acts as a snubber to lock the boom in traveling position.

SLEEK MODEL RACER

Cut the wheels out of a piece of 6/4 pine stock. As this stock measures 1⅜-in. thick, boring from both sides is required because the typical hole saw penetrates only ¾ in. deep.

Cut the body from a piece of 2x4. Use a band saw or a rip handsaw to cut the long taper. Drill ³⁄₂₆-in.-dia. holes for the lagscrew axles and ⁵⁄₁₆-in.-dia. holes for the roll bar. Drill the axle holes from both sides unless you have a long drill bit.

Paint the wheels and body. Select a suitable plastic bubble from a hardware package and carefully remove the backing. The bubble shown contained brads mounted on cardboard. Cut a cowl from ⅛-in. plywood or stiff cardboard, sized to fit over the bubble flange. Paint it, then nail it into place.

For a sporty touch, apply striping tape of a contrasting color.

USING A 2-in. hole saw in a drill press, you can cut the racer wheels from 6/4 stock.

Key	No.	MATERIALS LIST—RACER
		Size and description (use)
A	1	1⅜ × 3½ × 13" 2 × 4 fir (body)
B	4	1⅜ × 1⅞"-dia. 6/4 pine (wheels)
C	1	Plastic bubble from hardware package (canopy)
D	1	⅛" plywood (cowl)
E	1	⁵⁄₁₆ × 2½" U-bolt (roll bar)
F	8	⁵⁄₁₆" i.d. washer
G	4	¼ × 2½" lagscrews
H		Striping tape (as reqd.)

SAND WHEELS and check for fit. Accessories include U-bolt, plastic bubble.

VINYL STRIPING tape has pressure-sensitive backing. Strips come precut.

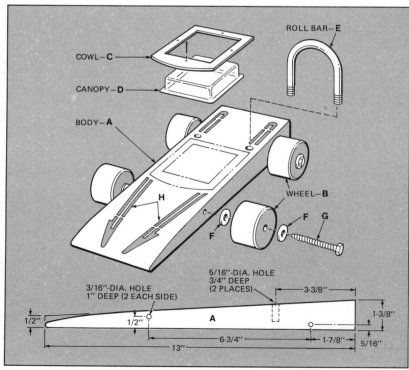

PLAY CENTER TV

Cut the plywood to size, then draw three rectangles for the cutouts. Draw three straight lines the length of the top and side of the smaller opening and the side of the large opening. Drive in one nail at each end of these lines. Place the flexible guide against the standing nails, then deflect it ½ in. at the center and trace the line.

Bore 2-in.-dia. holes tangent to the outline to form the round corners and make the cuts with a sabre saw.

Carefully cut the ½-in.-wide slots at the bottom of the board and in the tops of the base pieces to produce neat interlocking joints.

Sand and paint all the parts before assembly. Use a chalkboard paint on the hardboard. Use flathead screws with finishing washers to attach the hardboard and bulletin board. The shelf is attached last.

Self-adhering plastic clothing hooks are attached to the bulletin board material.

FLEXIBLE RULE is used to draw the pattern for curved cutouts (left). Rule is deflected ½ in. at center. Holes (right) made with a 2-in. hole saw form corners of the cutouts.

Key	No.	Size and description (use)
		MATERIALS LIST—PLAY TV
A	1	½ × 48 × 52″ plywood (frame)
B	2	½ × 12 × 24″ plywood (foot)
C	1	½ × 3 × 19″ plywood (shelf)
D	2	½ × 4 × 5″ plywood (shelf end)
E	2	½ × 1 × 5″ plywood (shelf cleat)
F	1	½ × 19 × 38″ cork-faced Homasote (bulletin board)
G	1	⅓ × 19 × 23″ chalkboard
H	2	⅞ × 44″ wood outside corner-guard molding (frame edging)
I	1	1⅛ × 19″ wood outside corner-guard molding (shelf edging)
J	1	8 × 10″ mirror
K	1	24″ shade with brackets
L	3	Dial knobs, Amerock T-594
M	1	No. 6 countersunk washers
N	14	¾″ No. 6 fh screws
O	4	⅞″ No. 6 fh screws
P	16	1″ No. 6 fh screws
Q	1	4d finishing nails
R	4	Coat hooks (self-sticking plastic type)

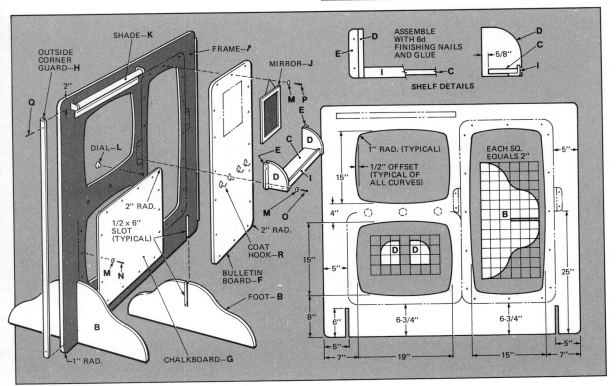

A 7° BEVEL is cut along both edges (left). Note that, after you have cut one side, board must be flopped before cutting second edge to insure that bevel angle is properly positioned. 35° bevel on top of cradle sides is cut (right) after pieces have been separated.

18TH-CENTURY DOLL CRADLE

Select a piece of warp-free 1x12 pine and draw on the cradle sides. Make the bevel cuts along both edges of the board before cutting out the sides so you will have a straight edge to ride the fence. Cut the 35° bevel on the tops, then smooth all exposed edges except the bevels.

Next, cut the footboard, headboard, canopy support and rockers. Then cut the canopy parts to size with the appropriate bevels. Sand before assembly.

To assemble, glue and nail the sides to the footboard and headboard, using 6d finishing nails. Attach rockers to the bottom, then join the bottom to the sides. Attach the canopy support and the canopy pieces. Set all nailheads and fill.

We obtained an antique finish using ordinary stain. Apply a diluted coat of sanding sealer, let it dry, then sand lightly. Next, wipe on a satin stain and stroke it lightly with a cloth to produce a grained effect. Allow twice the normal drying time, then finish with polyurethane varnish.

MATERIALS LIST—DOLL CRADLE		
Key	**No.**	**Size and description (use)**
A	1	¾ × 10¾ × 22½" pine (bottom)
B	1	¾ × 11¼ × 13¹¹⁄₁₆" pine (headboard)
C	2	¾ × 11¼ × 22½" pine (sides)
D	2	¾ × 3½ × 18³⁄₈" pine (rockers)
E	1	¾ × 6¾ × 9¾" pine (footboard)
F	1	¾ × 3¾ × 11¼" pine (canopy support)
G	2	¾ × 5⁹⁄₁₆ × 6⁷⁄₈" pine (canopy side)
H	1	¾ × 5¾ × 6⁷⁄₈" pine (canopy top)
Misc.: 6d finishing nails and glue.		

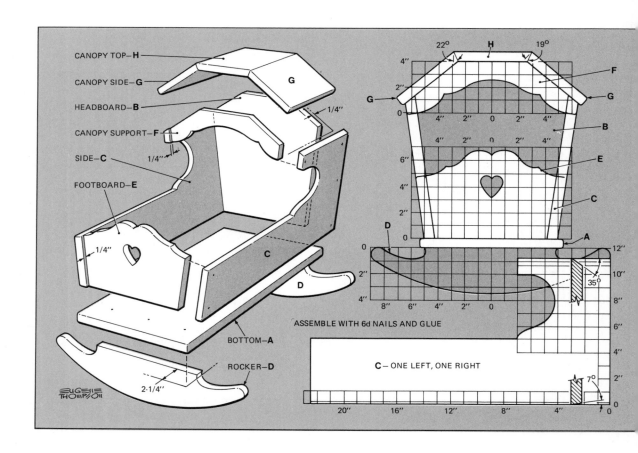

Heirloom wagon

■ THIS STURDY CHILD'S WAGON is built of solid oak to last for generations. It features a smooth-operating steering mechanism of a Lazy Susan.

Start by cutting all parts as shown. Make all 1½-in.-thick parts by gluing up two pieces of ¾-in. stock. Next, cut box joints into the wagon sides and ends using a box-joint jig on a table saw or router table. Attach the six floorboards with 1½-in., No. 8 roundhead brass screws. Leave a ¼-in. space between the boards.

Next, glue and shape the front and rear suspensions. Then clamp the end caps to each suspension and bore a ½-in.-dia. hole for the axle. Remove the end caps and bore out all parts to hold a hexnut.

Reassemble the parts with the nuts embedded. Assemble the steering mechanism with the Lazy Susan in position. Then bore through the floorboard, steering tongue and front suspension to install the pivot bolt. Bore and chisel out the mortise in the handle block. Secure the handle by driving in two wedges. Attach the remaining parts and connect the wheels by screwing the axles into embedded nuts. Apply a waterproof finish.

MATERIALS LIST
HEIRLOOM WAGON

Key	No.	Size and description (use)
A	2	¾ x 4½ x 36" oak (sides)
B	2	¾ x 4½ x 18" oak (ends)
C	5	¾ x 6½ x 18" oak (floor)
C1	1	¾ x 2¼ x 18" oak (floor)
D	2	¾ x 2½ x 26" oak (side rails)
E	1	¾ x 2½ x 18" oak (back rail)
F	6	¾ x 1¼ x 8½" oak (supports)
G	1	1½ x 6 x 14" (rear suspension)
G1	1	1½ x 5¹¹⁄₁₆ x 14" oak (front suspension)
H	4	¾ x 1½ x 3" oak (end caps)
I	1	1½ x 4 x 18" oak (steering tongue)
J	1	¾ x 1½ x 32" oak (steering post)
J1	2	¼ x ½ x 1⅝" maple (wedge)
K	1	1½ x 1⅝ x 3" oak (handle block)
L	2	¾"-dia. x 5" oak (handles)
L1	2	½ x 1¼"-dia. oak (handle caps)
M	1	⁵⁄₁₆ x 6" Lazy Susan
N	6	½" No. 6 flathead screws with washers
O	1	½"-dia. x 6" carriage bolt, 3 washers and locknut (handle pivot)
P	6	¼"-dia. x 3" lagscrew and washer
Q		1½" No. 8 oval or roundhead brass screws
R	4	8"-dia. wheel with ball bearing
S	4	½"-dia. x 6" carriage bolts, two washers and locknuts (axle)
T	1	¼"-dia. x 4" carriage bolts, washers, locknuts

Misc.: Carpenter's glue, pinstripe tape, sandpaper, waterproof finish or marine varnish.

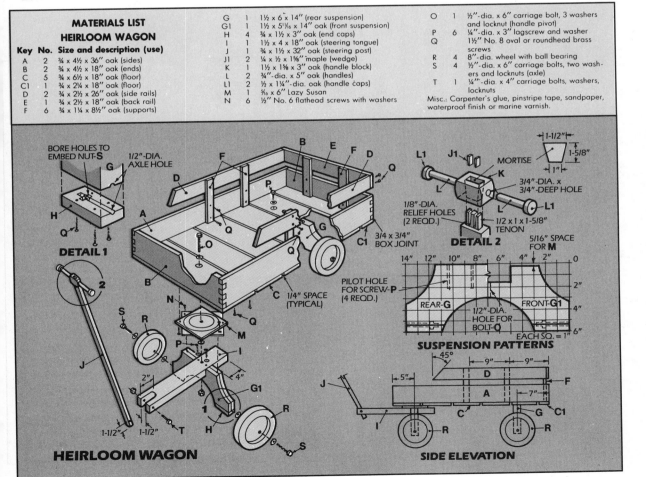

It's fun to make toys

■ THIS TOY BOX is a classy little circus wagon that will add color to any youngster's room.

Sides of the wagon are carbon copies. The holes for the nine bars are drilled before the top and bottom members are sabre-sawed. In fact, each side can be made a simple rectangular frame to start before any of the pieces are bored and sawed. If you have a doweling jig, use it to bore mating holes dead-center and 3 in. apart. Make a full-size pattern from the half pattern given and trace the curves on your wood. For perfect alignment, drill the holes for the ¾-in. dowel axles through both side assemblies at one time. Enlarge the holes slightly with a round file or sandpaper wrapped around a dowel.

The 7-in. wheels consist of two plywood discs and a hub. The spokes are jigsawed first, then the ¼-in. thickness is glued to the ½ in. and both are sawed round as one. The hubs are centered and glued to the wheels, then ¾-in. holes are bored through both hub and ½-in. disc.

Circus-wagon toy box

Giraffe clothes tree

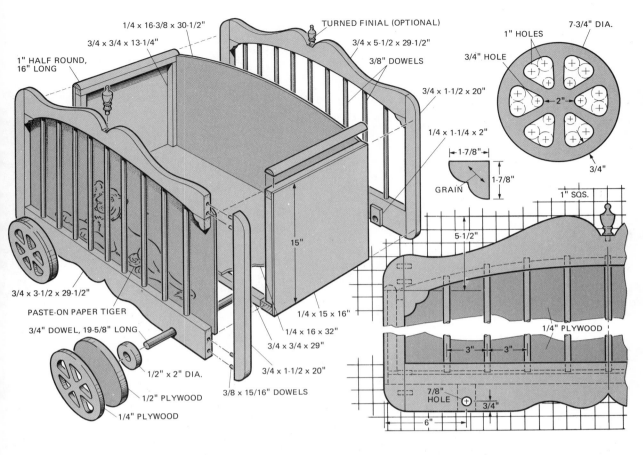

TURNED FINIAL (OPTIONAL)

1/4 x 16-3/8 x 30-1/2"

3/4 x 3/4 x 13-1/4"

1" HALF ROUND, 16" LONG

3/4 x 5-1/2 x 29-1/2"

3/8" DOWELS

3/4 x 1-1/2 x 20"

1/4 x 1-1/4 x 2"

1-7/8"

1-7/8"

GRAIN

7-3/4" DIA.

1" HOLES

3/4" HOLE

2"

3/4"

15"

1" SQS.

5-1/2"

3/4 x 3-1/2 x 29-1/2"

PASTE-ON PAPER TIGER

3/4" DOWEL, 19-5/8" LONG

1/2" x 2" DIA.

1/2" PLYWOOD

1/4" PLYWOOD

1/4 x 15 x 16"

1/4 x 16 x 32"

3/4 x 3/4 x 29"

3/4 x 1-1/2 x 20"

3/8 x 15/16" DOWELS

3" 3"

1/4" PLYWOOD

7/8" HOLE

3/4"

6"

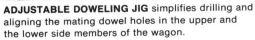

ADJUSTABLE DOWELING JIG simplifies drilling and aligning the mating dowel holes in the upper and the lower side members of the wagon.

AFTER HOLES are bored, the curves in the top and the bottom members are then cut with a sabre saw. With dowel bars in place, the ends are added.

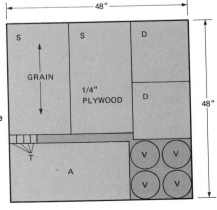

48"

S   S   D

GRAIN

1/4" PLYWOOD

D

48"

T

A

V   V

V   V

Cutting layout

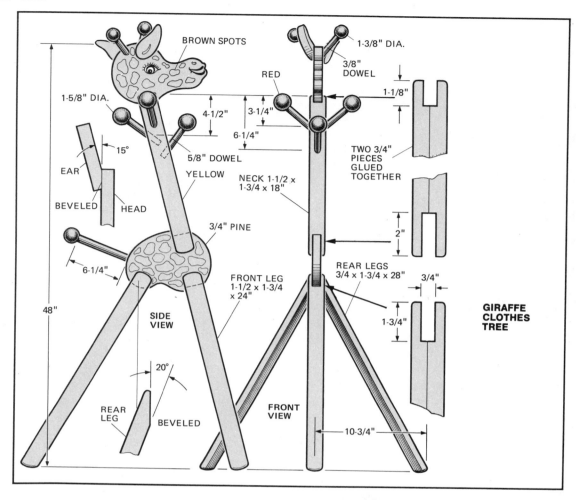

The completed sides are glued to a simple ¼-in. plywood box and the cutting layout shows how the five parts can be laid out economically on a 4x4-ft. panel with wood to spare for the wheels. They are glued to ¾-in.-square members which are placed inside the ends and under the bottom. Sides of the cage are finally glued to the box; then panels S are painted white, and the paper tigers are attached with rubber cement and finally nailed in place behind the bars. Wheels are glued to the dowel axles to complete the project.

He'll hold their clothes

You'll be surprised how this long-necked, three-legged fellow can get little ones to hang up their clothes. Sawing the head, body and ears is hardest; the rest is easy. Ears are beveled on the inside to point outward when glued in place. Front leg and neck are two 1x2 pieces notched at ends, then glued together. Balls on ends of the pegs are wood finials you'll find at lumberyards and craft centers. Note that the top balls are

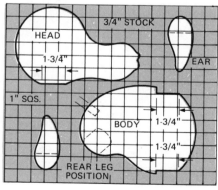

smaller than others. Paint the clothes tree yellow and add brown spots to look like a giraffe.

Any child's favorite

Next to a doll, a dollhouse is perhaps the most wanted gift for any little girl. On the following page is a simple one you can make in a weekend. It's designed after an early 19th century English

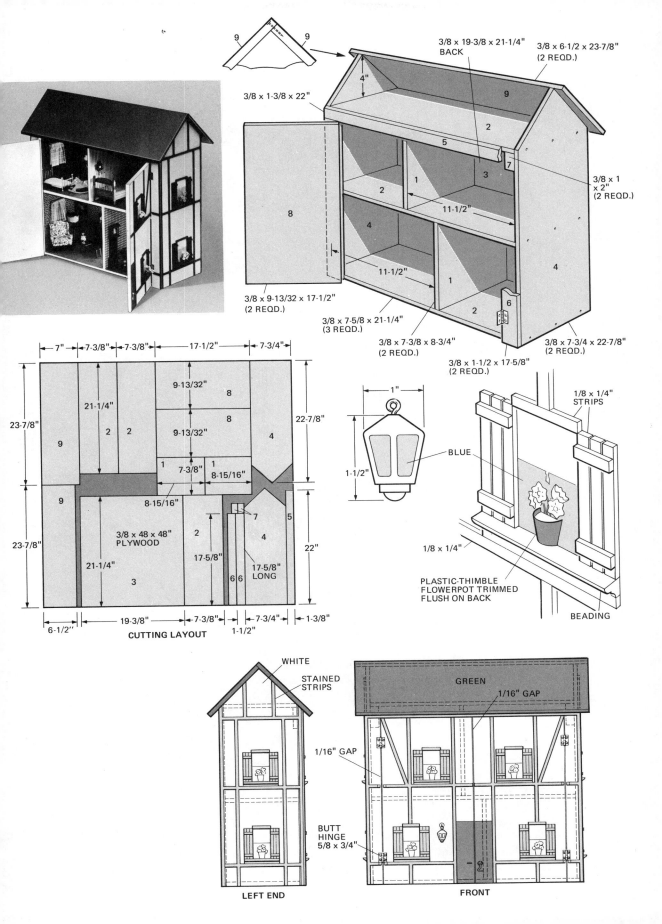

3/8 x 19-3/8 x 21-1/4"
BACK

3/8 x 6-1/2 x 23-7/8"
(2 REQD.)

3/8 x 1-3/8 x 22"

4"

9

2

5

3

1

2

7

3/8 x 1
x 2"
(2 REQD.)

11-1/2"

4

1

4

11-1/2"

1

4

2

6

3/8 x 9-13/32 x 17-1/2"
(2 REQD.)

8

3/8 x 7-5/8 x 21-1/4"
(3 REQD.)

3/8 x 7-3/8 x 8-3/4"
(2 REQD.)

3/8 x 1-1/2 x 17-5/8"
(2 REQD.)

3/8 x 7-3/4 x 22-7/8"
(2 REQD.)

Cutting Layout

7" 7-3/8" 7-3/8" 17-1/2" 7-3/4"

23-7/8"

9-13/32" 8

9-13/32" 8

21-1/4"
2 2

4

22-7/8"

9

1 7-3/8" 1
8-15/16"

8-15/16"

23-7/8"

9

3/8 x 48 x 48"
PLYWOOD

2

17-5/8"

7

4

5

21-1/4"

3

17-5/8"
LONG

6 6

22"

6-1/2" 19-3/8" 7-3/8" 7-3/4" 1-3/8"

1-1/2"

CUTTING LAYOUT

1"

1-1/2"

BLUE

1/8 x 1/4"
STRIPS

1/8 x 1/4"

PLASTIC-THIMBLE
FLOWERPOT TRIMMED
FLUSH ON BACK

BEADING

WHITE

STAINED
STRIPS

GREEN

1/16" GAP

1/16" GAP

BUTT
HINGE
5/8 x 3/4"

LEFT END

FRONT

B
1/2" BLIND HOLE
EACH SIDE FOR LEAD SHOT

1/16" THICK EYE

WOOD BEAD

3/4"

1" SQS.

GRAY

3/4" PINE

3" RAD.

PULL CORD

A

1-1/4" RAD.

7/8" THICK

1/4 x 2 x 9"

2-1/4"

1-3/16"

3/4"

SIDE VIEW

END VIEW
(BLOCK A REMOVED)

1/2"

BLUE

RED

A

WASHER

3/4 x 1-1/2 x 5-3/8"

B

3/4"

RH SCREW

3/4 x 2-1/4 x 9"

7/8"

STATIONARY JAW AND END BLOCK

1/2" DOWEL

1/16" WASHER

1/2" HOLE

1/2" HOLE

1/2 x 2-1/2" WHEELS

CAM
1/2 x 1-1/2" DIA.

1/4 x 1-1/2 x 1-3/4"
AXLE BRACKET

RUBBER BAND

UNDERSIDE VIEW shows how cam on dow
axle opens and closes the whale's mouth.

HALE THE WHALE

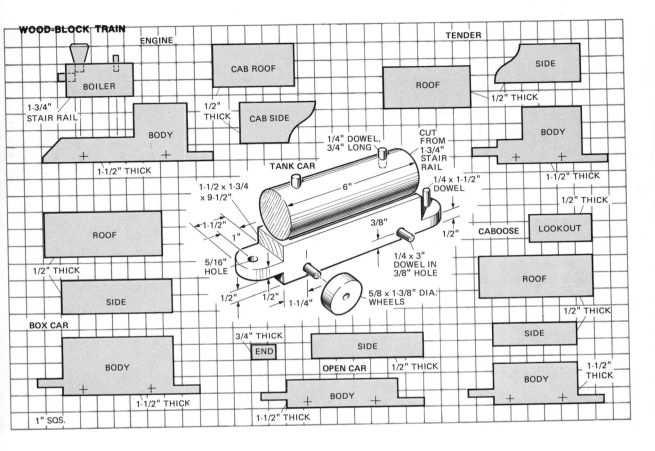

WOOD-BLOCK TRAIN

ENGINE

TENDER

BOILER

1-3/4" STAIR RAIL

CAB ROOF

1/2" THICK

CAB SIDE

ROOF

SIDE

1/2" THICK

BODY

1-1/2" THICK

BODY

1-1/2" THICK

1/2" THICK

TANK CAR

1/4" DOWEL, 3/4" LONG

CUT FROM 1-3/4" STAIR RAIL

1/4 x 1-1/2" DOWEL

1-1/2 x 1-3/4 x 9-1/2"

6"

1-1/2"

1"

3/8"

1/2"

5/16" HOLE

1/4 x 3" DOWEL IN 3/8" HOLE

CABOOSE

LOOKOUT

ROOF

1/2" THICK

SIDE

1/2" THICK

1/2" 1/2" 1-1/4"

5/8 x 1-3/8" DIA. WHEELS

ROOF

1/2" THICK

BOX CAR

3/4" THICK

END

SIDE

1/2" THICK

SIDE

BODY

1-1/2" THICK

OPEN CAR

BODY

1-1/2" THICK

1" SQS.

BODY

1-1/2" THICK

---

farmhouse. The front opens wide to provide full access to four rooms.

The 17 parts can be cut from a 4x4-ft. piece of ⅜-in. plywood. Follow the diagram when laying out the parts, but follow the dimensions when cutting.

Start assembly by nailing and gluing the three floors to one end, inserting partitions as you go. Then add the second end and the back. Glue parts 7 next, then part 5, and parts 6. Hinge panels 8 to the front and add the roof.

Paint the house white; then decorate ends and front with stained wood strips as shown in front and end views. Paint on windows and doors and fit them with shutters, window boxes and plastic thimble flowerpots.

Puff puff engine

Puff puff engine is a toy which puffs "smoke" as it is pulled along. The illusion is created by a 7-in. clear plastic disc which rests on two inner wheels and turns clockwise when the wheels turn. Four "puffs" of blue tape are stuck to each side of the plastic disc at 12, 3, 6 and 9 o'clock, and a ⅛-in. wire shaft in an elongated center hole holds the disc in place.

The body is a sandwich of five layers, two ¾-in. thick, two ½-in. and one ¼ in. Spacers A and B form the ¼-in.-wide slot for the disc. The ½-in. pieces are made right and left hand, and the cab's roof is slotted for the disc. Blind holes are made in the four drive wheels and the wheels glued to their axles.

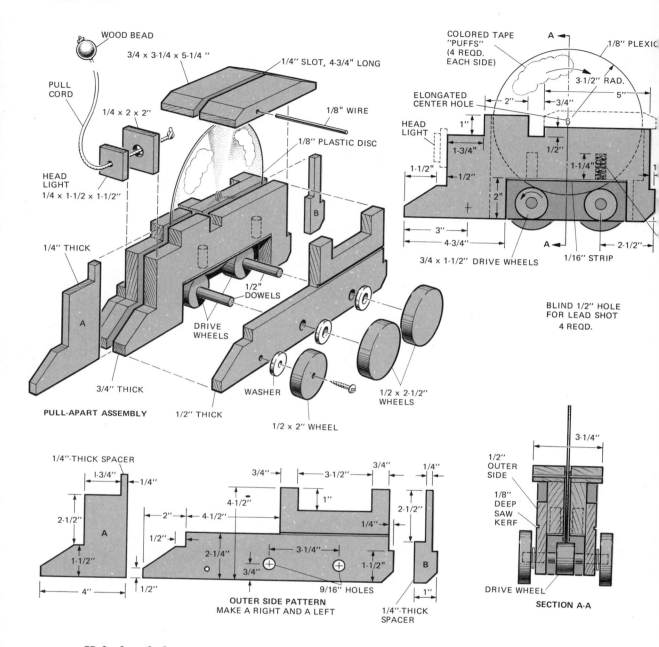

WOOD BEAD

3/4 x 3-1/4 x 5-1/4 ''

1/4" SLOT, 4-3/4" LONG

PULL CORD

1/4 x 2 x 2''

1/8" WIRE

1/8" PLASTIC DISC

HEAD LIGHT
1/4 x 1-1/2 x 1-1/2''

B

1/4" THICK

A

1/2" DOWELS

DRIVE WHEELS

3/4" THICK

WASHER

1/2 x 2-1/2'' WHEELS

PULL-APART ASSEMBLY

1/2" THICK

1/2 x 2" WHEEL

COLORED TAPE "PUFFS" (4 REQD. EACH SIDE)

A

1/8" PLEXIC

3-1/2" RAD.

ELONGATED CENTER HOLE

2"

3/4"

5"

HEAD LIGHT

1"

1/2"

1-3/4"

1-1/4"

1-1/2"

1/2"

2"

3"

A

4-3/4"

2-1/2"

3/4 x 1-1/2'' DRIVE WHEELS

1/16" STRIP

BLIND 1/2" HOLE FOR LEAD SHOT 4 REQD.

1/4"-THICK SPACER

1-3/4"

1/4"

2-1/2"

A

1-1/2"

4"

1/2"

3/4"

3-1/2"

3/4"

1/4"

4-1/2"

1"

2"

4-1/2"

2-1/2"

1/4"

1/2"

2-1/4"

3-1/4"

1-1/2"

3/4"

9/16" HOLES

OUTER SIDE PATTERN
MAKE A RIGHT AND A LEFT

B

1"

1/4"-THICK SPACER

1/2" OUTER SIDE

1/8" DEEP SAW KERF

3-1/4"

DRIVE WHEEL

SECTION A-A

Hale the whale

Opening and closing his mouth as he swims along at the end of a string, Hale the Whale is an irresistible toy small fry will go for in a big way. A wood cam between the front wheels works the mouth up and down as the toy is pulled; 7/8-in. spacer blocks A and B allow free movement for the 3/4-in. pivoted body.

A circle cutter in a drill press will cut the 1/2-in.-thick plywood wheels quickly. Round-head screws serve as axles for the rear wheels; blind holes in the front wheels fit the dowel axle and the wheels are glued on. Enlarge holes in the brackets slightly so the axle turns freely.

Fast freight from scrap wood

Youngsters always like trains for Christmas. The wood-block freight train can be made from scrap found in your woodbox. If you plan to make several as gifts, it will pay you to buy a length of 1⅜-in. wood closet pole and slice the ¾-in. wheels from it. Likewise a length of 1¾-in. stair rail will save time in making several engine boilers and tanks for tank cars.

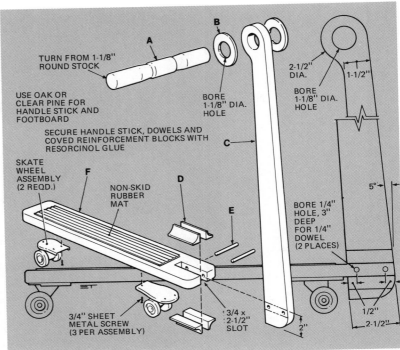

TURN FROM 1-1/8" ROUND STOCK

A

B

C

D

E

F

USE OAK OR CLEAR PINE FOR HANDLE STICK AND FOOTBOARD

SECURE HANDLE STICK, DOWELS AND COVED REINFORCEMENT BLOCKS WITH RESORCINOL GLUE

SKATE WHEEL ASSEMBLY (2 REQD.)

NON-SKID RUBBER MAT

BORE 1-1/8" DIA. HOLE

2-1/2" DIA.

1-1/2"

BORE 1-1/8" DIA. HOLE

5°

BORE 1/4" HOLE, 3" DEEP FOR 1/4" DOWEL (2 PLACES)

3/4" SHEET METAL SCREW (3 PER ASSEMBLY)

3/4 x 2-1/2" SLOT

2"

1/2"

2-1/2"

Scooters from skates

■ THIS ROLLER-SKATE scooter is fun both for tots too small to safely use skateboards and for older ones who ride at full speed. Since fixed wheels give it a limited turning radius, there is little danger of the scooter veering sharply.

Using scrap wood and an old pair of roller skates, you can make two of these scooters in short order. Separate the wheel assemblies from the skates and remove or cut off projections from the flat mounting plates. Drill three holes in each plate for attaching to the footboard.

Cut pieces itemized in the materials list from 1-in. scrap wood. Or modify dimensions to suit stock on hand and size of user. Round the lower edge of the handle post to ride over small obstacles. Slightly round and sand all edges.

Turn the handle grip from 1⅛-in.-dia. round stock. Glue the grip into the hole in the handle post, along with a plywood washer on both sides to strengthen assembly.

Draw a centerline on underside of the footboard to position the wheel assemblies but do not attach them yet. Locate the front wheels as close as possible to the handle slot. Position the rear wheels at the very end of the footboard. Hold a straight-edge against the sides of a front and a rear wheel to keep the assemblies aligned while marking for screws. Make holes for the mounting screws with an awl, but don't install them.

Secure the handle post in the footboard slot with glue and dowels. Reinforce this joint at the four 90° corners by gluing in 2½-in.-long pieces of ¾x¾-in. cove stock.

Sand assembly, round all sharp corners and fill dents with wood putty. Finish with exterior paint.

When paint dries, attach the wheel assemblies. Glue rubber padding to top of the footboard for nonslip footing.

MATERIALS LIST—SCOOTER

Key	Pcs.	Size and description (use)
A	1	1⅛"-dia. x 8" hardwood (handle grip)
B	2	¼ x 2½"-dia. (shop-made washers)
C	1	¾ x 2½ x 27" (handle post)
D	4	¾ x ¾ x 2½" (cove reinforcement blocks)
E	2	¼"-dia. x 3"-long dowels
F	1	¾ x 4 x 20" (footboard)

Misc.: Resorcinol glue; ¾-in. No. 6 sheet metal screws; 1 roller skate; piece of nonskid rubber mat.

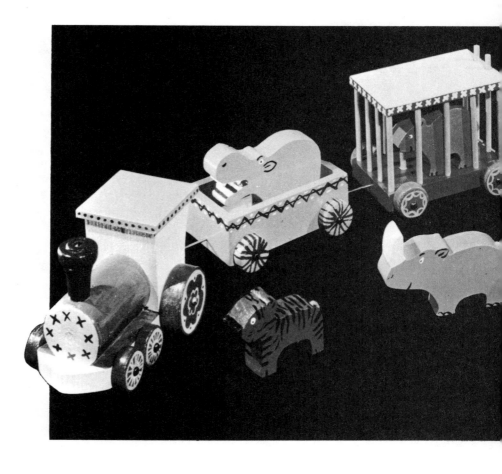

Pull-toy circus train

■ CHUGGING ALONG at the end of a string, this colorful little circus train will bring shrieks of delight from any two or three-year-old. All you'll need to buy to make the train are a few screws, screw eyes, L-hooks, a couple of dowels and some *nontoxic* paint. The wood should be available in your workshop scrap box.

If you make it five cars long, the train will carry the 10 animals, each car holding two. If you own a lathe, you can quickly turn such parts as the engine's smokestack and boiler, as well as the wheels. However, if you don't have a lathe, the smokestack can be turned with your electric drill. Drill a wood block lengthwise, slip it over a bolt, tighten with a nut and chuck the end of the bolt in the drill. Cradle the drill in a vise and rig up a second block as a rest for your chisel. You

can "turn" the wheels without a lathe by using a hole cutter in your drill or drill press.

Use glue and small finishing nails to assemble the cars and sand the edges smooth. In the case of the cage car, the two holes for the ½-in. "gate bars" go all the way through the roof and are 5/16 in. for a loose fit. The ends of the gate bars are pointed so they seat automatically in the holes, and ½-in. lengths of small dowel are inserted crosswise to prevent the bars from being pulled all the way out. The holes for the three center dowels, which provide stalls, are drilled in the base only. All other matching holes are spaced and drilled the same in both base and roof.

To simplify things, it's best to paint the roof and base before gluing the dowels in place. The

dowels are left unpainted. Round the outer edges of the wheels with sandpaper, paint the designs on them and attach them to the wagons with roundhead wood screws so they will turn freely. The photo will serve as a guide when you paint the wagons and add the fancy designs on their roofs, sides and wheels in bright colors.

An L-hook is turned into one end of each car and a screw eye in the other; screw eyes are used at each end of the engine. The engine cab is sawed from either a solid or glued-up block.

The animals are sawed from 1 or 1⅛-in. pine with either a bandsaw or jigsaw, and ⅛-in. holes are drilled for tasseled and braided tails of yarn. For safety's sake, it's important that you use nontoxic paint and anchor the yarn tails firmly in their holes.

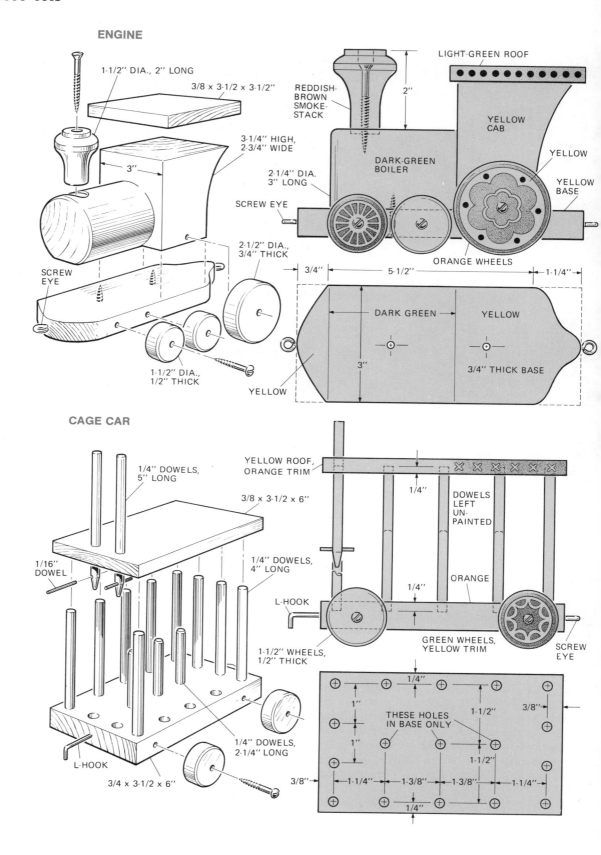

ENGINE

1-1/2'' DIA., 2'' LONG

3/8 x 3-1/2 x 3-1/2''

REDDISH-BROWN SMOKE-STACK

LIGHT-GREEN ROOF

2''

YELLOW CAB

3-1/4'' HIGH, 2-3/4'' WIDE

3''

2-1/4'' DIA. 3'' LONG

DARK-GREEN BOILER

YELLOW

YELLOW BASE

SCREW EYE

SCREW EYE

2-1/2'' DIA., 3/4'' THICK

ORANGE WHEELS

3/4''

5-1/2''

1-1/4''

DARK GREEN

YELLOW

1-1/2'' DIA., 1/2'' THICK

3''

3/4'' THICK BASE

YELLOW

CAGE CAR

1/4'' DOWELS, 5'' LONG

YELLOW ROOF, ORANGE TRIM

3/8 x 3-1/2 x 6''

1/4''

DOWELS LEFT UN-PAINTED

1/16'' DOWEL

1/4'' DOWELS, 4'' LONG

L-HOOK

ORANGE

1/4''

1-1/2'' WHEELS, 1/2'' THICK

GREEN WHEELS, YELLOW TRIM

SCREW EYE

1/4'' DOWELS, 2-1/4'' LONG

1/4''

1''

1-1/2''

3/8''

L-HOOK

THESE HOLES IN BASE ONLY

3/4 x 3-1/2 x 6''

1''

1-1/2''

3/8''

1-1/4''

1-3/8''

1-3/8''

1-1/4''

1/4''

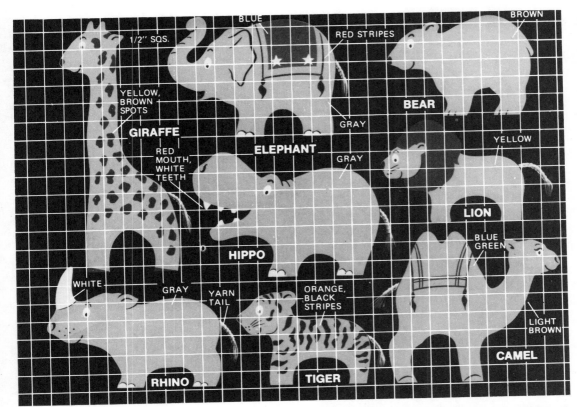

1/2" SQS.

BLUE

RED STRIPES

BROWN

YELLOW, BROWN SPOTS

GIRAFFE

BEAR

GRAY

YELLOW

RED MOUTH, WHITE TEETH

ELEPHANT

GRAY

LION

HIPPO

BLUE GREEN

WHITE

GRAY

YARN TAIL

ORANGE, BLACK STRIPES

LIGHT BROWN

CAMEL

RHINO

TIGER

GIRAFFE CAR

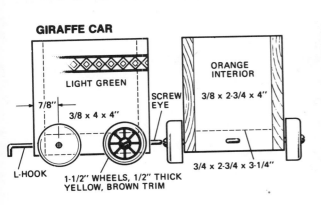

LIGHT GREEN

3/8 x 4 x 4"

7/8"

SCREW EYE

ORANGE INTERIOR

3/8 x 2-3/4 x 4"

L-HOOK

1-1/2" WHEELS, 1/2" THICK
YELLOW, BROWN TRIM

3/4 x 2-3/4 x 3-1/4"

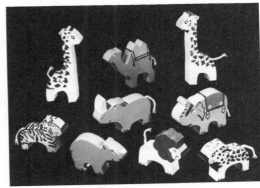

BOXCAR

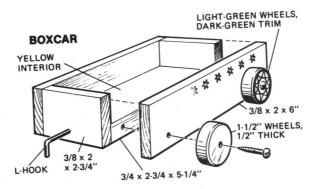

LIGHT-GREEN WHEELS,
DARK-GREEN TRIM

YELLOW INTERIOR

3/8 x 2 x 6"

1-1/2" WHEELS,
1/2" THICK

L-HOOK

3/8 x 2 x 2-3/4"

3/4 x 2-3/4 x 5-1/4"

Kitchen appliances for your youngster

■ STURDY, REALISTIC-LOOKING and sure to please your youngster is this set of pint-sized kitchen appliances you can build in a weekend or two. Unlike the flimsy metal or corrugated cardboard counterparts available commercially, these scaled-down versions of major appliances have enough movable parts to keep a child occupied for months.

Because the units are constructed of pine stock and skinned with ¼-in. chip and hardboard, they are light enough to be easily moved, yet rugged enough to take the punishment small fry can dish out. All units are assembled using glue as well as nails. To fasten the outer covering, also use white glue and ¾-in. finishing nails.

Since the three units are basically alike, you can save time by using jigs, gang-cutting and other production-line methods wherever possible. For example, after roughing out the hardboard and chipboard, all frame pieces of a given dimension can be clamped together and cut simultaneously on the table saw. To avoid confusion, mark all pieces as they are cut. With all pieces of the frames cut, these parts can be sanded and prime painted prime those areas that will be glue-joined.

Range

To mark the range for the clocks and dials as shown, use a center punch to locate exact centers. After painting the front, the circles, clock dials and other details can be applied using India ink and an artist's brush. When this "artwork" is dry, apply clear varnish. The window on the chipboard door is simply a piece of acrylic set in the rabbet with bathtub caulk.

THE MINIATURE KITCHEN furniture consists of a two-door refrigerator, a sink with faucet, and a stove with play dials and an oven. All are constructed alike—¼-in. chipboard over ¾ x 1¼-in. framework. Appliances can be painted to match your full-size ones.

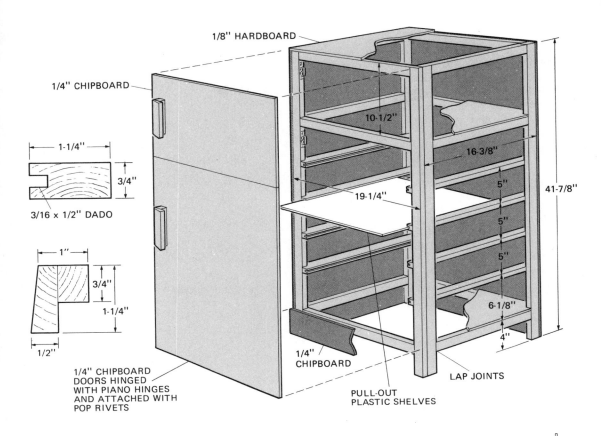

1/8" HARDBOARD

1/4" CHIPBOARD

1-1/4"

3/4"

3/16 x 1/2" DADO

1"

3/4"

1-1/4"

1/2"

1/4" CHIPBOARD
DOORS HINGED
WITH PIANO HINGES
AND ATTACHED WITH
POP RIVETS

10-1/2"

16-3/8"

19-1/4"

5"

5"

5"

6-1/8"

4"

41-7/8"

1/4"
CHIPBOARD

PULL-OUT
PLASTIC SHELVES

LAP JOINTS

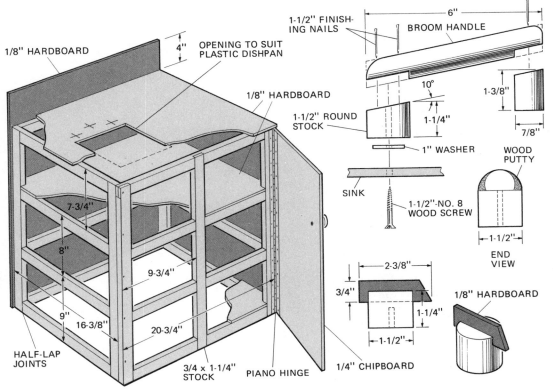

1/8" HARDBOARD

4"

OPENING TO SUIT
PLASTIC DISHPAN

1/8" HARDBOARD

7-3/4"

8"

9-3/4"

9"

16-3/8"

20-3/4"

HALF-LAP
JOINTS

3/4 x 1-1/4"
STOCK

PIANO HINGE

1-1/2" FINISH-
ING NAILS

BROOM HANDLE

6"

1-1/2" ROUND
STOCK

10°

1-1/4"

1-3/8"

7/8"

1" WASHER

SINK

1-1/2"-NO. 8
WOOD SCREW

WOOD
PUTTY

1-1/2"

END
VIEW

2-3/8"

3/4"

1-1/4"

1-1/2"

1/4" CHIPBOARD

1/8" HARDBOARD

Sink

On the unit shown, the sink is a 2¼ x 7½ x 7½-in. bowl that came with a 49-cent vegetable grater. Before cutting out your sinktop, have your "sink" on hand to assure a neat fit. The sink trim requires a little effort using a chisel and coping saw to do the notching. After assembling these parts, fill any voids with a wood filler and sand smooth. Trim can be finish-painted with aluminum paint for realism.

Refrigerator

This is the easiest unit to construct because it is really just a box with two doors. As with all units, sand all surfaces and edges absolutely smooth before applying a *nontoxic paint*.

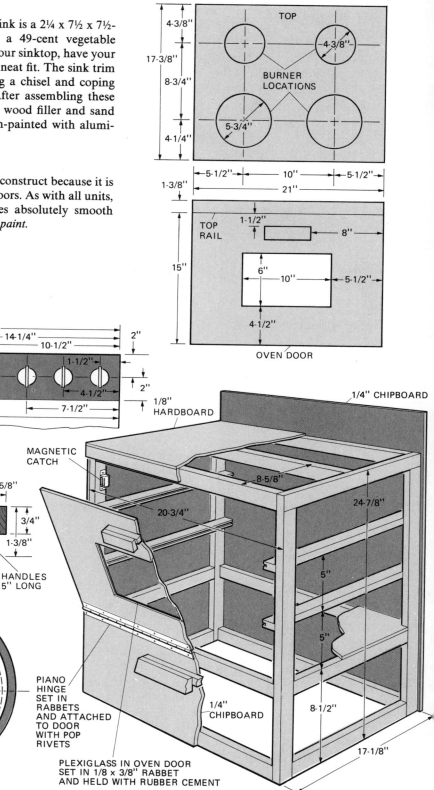

TOP

BURNER LOCATIONS

4-3/8"
4-3/8"
17-3/8"
8-3/4"
5-3/4"
4-1/4"
5-1/2"
10"
5-1/2"
21"
1-3/8"

TOP RAIL
1-1/2"
8"
6"
10"
5-1/2"
4-1/2"

OVEN DOOR

CLOCK
TIMER
18-1/2"
14-1/4"
10-1/2"
2"
1-1/2"
2"
4-1/2"
3"
3"
7-1/2"
21"
1/8" HARDBOARD

2"
1/4"
1/2"
1-1/2"
KNOB (MAKE 5)

3/8" 5/8"
3/4"
1-3/8"
85°
1/2"
HANDLES 5" LONG

BURNER ELEMENT SAWED FROM 1/4" CHIPBOARD. MAKE 4

PAINTED RED

MAGNETIC CATCH

1/4" CHIPBOARD

8-5/8"
24-7/8"
20-3/4"
5"
5"

1/4" CHIPBOARD

8-1/2"
17-1/8"

PIANO HINGE SET IN RABBETS AND ATTACHED TO DOOR WITH POP RIVETS

PLEXIGLASS IN OVEN DOOR SET IN 1/8 x 3/8" RABBET AND HELD WITH RUBBER CEMENT

Toy dump truck

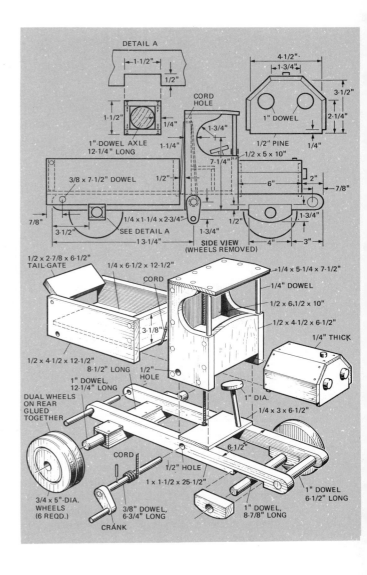

■ WHAT YOUNGSTER wouldn't think you're the greatest ever when surprised with this all-wood dump truck? It actually dumps with a turn of a crank, and it's built to take a beating.

Start work with the chassis and cut, notch and bore the two rails at one time. Bore both front axle blocks together so the holes align, and assemble the 8½-in. long square "tube" in which the rear axle turns.

Space the two rails 6½ in. with a 1-in. dowel at the front and the axle tube at the rear. Glue the axle blocks in the notches at the front and add the cab's floor and steering wheel. Single wheels are glued to the front axle; dual wheels to the rear.

Assemble the cab so it straddles the rails and floor. Make it complete with seat and bore a hole in the floor, seat and back for the winch cord. Use screws in counterbored holes, and then cap the heads with short pieces of dowel glued in the holes and sanded flush. Make the ends of the hood fit between the rails and cover them with ¼-in. pine. Drill for 1-in.-dowel headlights and for a ¼-in. radiator cap.

Inside width of the dump body should be 6⅝ in. so it fits over the rails and pivots freely on a dowel at the rear. The tailgate should also swing open freely. Finish with nontoxic paint or varnish, or let it remain as bare wood.

Toy plane for mini-pilots

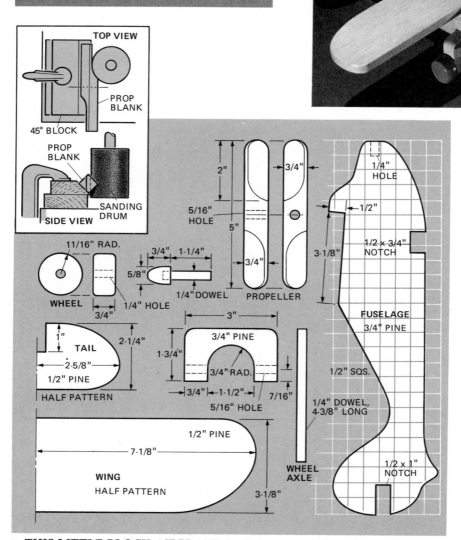

TOP VIEW

PROP BLANK

45° BLOCK

PROP BLANK

SANDING DRUM

SIDE VIEW

11/16" RAD.

WHEEL

3/4"

1/4" HOLE

3/4" — 1-1/4"

5/8"

1/4" DOWEL

2"

5/16" HOLE

5"

3/4"

3/4"

PROPELLER

1/4" HOLE

1/2"

1/2 x 3/4" NOTCH

3-1/8"

1/2" SQS.

FUSELAGE
3/4" PINE

1/4" DOWEL, 4-3/8" LONG

1/2 x 1" NOTCH

1"

TAIL

2-1/4"

2-5/8"

1/2" PINE

HALF PATTERN

3"

3/4" PINE

1-3/4"

3/4" RAD.

3/4" — 1-1/2"

5/16" HOLE

7/16"

WHEEL AXLE

1/2" PINE

7-1/8"

WING
HALF PATTERN

3-1/8"

■ **THIS LITTLE BLOCK AIRPLANE** for little aeronauts is a simple, nearly indestructible toy with just enough realism to excite their interest—including a prop that spins. It can be built in a couple of evenings. Wing and tail sections call for 2 feet of ½ x 6-in. clear pine; about 14 inches of 1 x 6 are needed for the fuselage. Propeller pin and wheel axle call for 8 inches of ¼-in. dowel. All remaining parts can be made from scraps of ¾-in. stock. Follow the plans below for dimensioning and cutting each piece. Sand all edges until round to avoid splinters. The propeller is easily made on a drill press. A plain block jig, beveled to 45°, is clamped to the table as shown. The ¾-in.-sq. blank is then held against the bevel and run past a sanding drum on the drill-press spindle. Leave enough hub for a 5/16-in. hole for prop pin and hub cowl. Assemble parts with brads and epoxy. The plane can be finished with clear finish or painted with a bright enamel.

You-haul kiddie car

■ THIS "YOU-HAUL" VERSION of the popular three-wheel kiddie car is a great toy for young truckers. The 1-in.-thick center frame consists of two pieces of ½-in. plywood. Bandsaw both pieces together, then glue and clamp them face to face and sand the edges. Make the 5-in. wheels, seat, floor and front of the stake body from plywood also. Cut the rest of the parts from hardwood such as birch.

If you don't have a wood lathe, the turned tenons on the ends of the rear axle can be formed by drilling the ends for 3-in. lengths of ½-in.

dowel. The turned steering handle can be made in a similar way. Slot the steering post for the front wheel and pivot the post to the center frame with two wood brackets and a loose-fitting dowel. Both brackets are glued and nailed in ⅜-in.-deep dadoes. Part A supports the rear axle in its ⅞-in. square notch, and a screw and washer are used to hold each wheel to the tenon. Make the holes in the wheels a bit larger than the tenons. A ⅜-in. dowel is the front axle, glued to the post. Drill a ½-in. hole in the wheel to make it turn freely and apply paste wax to tenons.

SAND all parts thoroughly, round all sharp edges. Paint with a non-toxic finish. Wheels, seat and handle can be red, the rest kept natural and given a coat of clear urethane. If you find that the seat needs extra support, a small wood bracket can be glued to each side and fastened to the seat with FH wood screws.

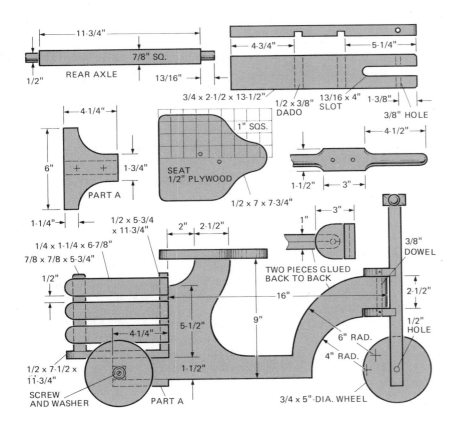

Hydraulic lift for your tractor

■ LIFTING A HEAVY bulldozer blade manually is for the birds even when it's only a fairly small one on a garden tractor. Pulling a lever to raise and lower the blade can make you arm-weary after only a few hours of grading or snow pushing. You can, however, add a hydraulic lift so a mere push of a button will lift and lower the blade.

The first step to add this pushbutton convenience was a trip to the local junkyard to pick up the power unit—a hydraulic system from the convertible top of a car. (The one selected happened to be from an Oldsmobile). Other parts included:

● Motor, pump, reservoir unit.
● Cylinder with bottom plate.
● Hydraulic hose.
● Wiring and dashboard switch for above motor.

As it turned out, one cylinder was sufficient to provide the muscle for the job. It does, in fact, effortlessly raise and lower the blade at a touch of the button, even with an average-size male sitting atop the blade.

Recognizing that prices can vary and probably will, depending upon the number of junkyards in a particular geographical location, a visit to your local junkyard for a materials price quote before starting the job is a practical approach.

Some changes on the manual lifting unit will be necessary so that the cylinder can be fitted in place. First, disassemble the lifting lever and linkage that connects it to the upper-lift frame. Then, using ¼ x 1¼ x 14¼-in. flat iron, make a flat brace (Detail F) and fasten it to the tractor.

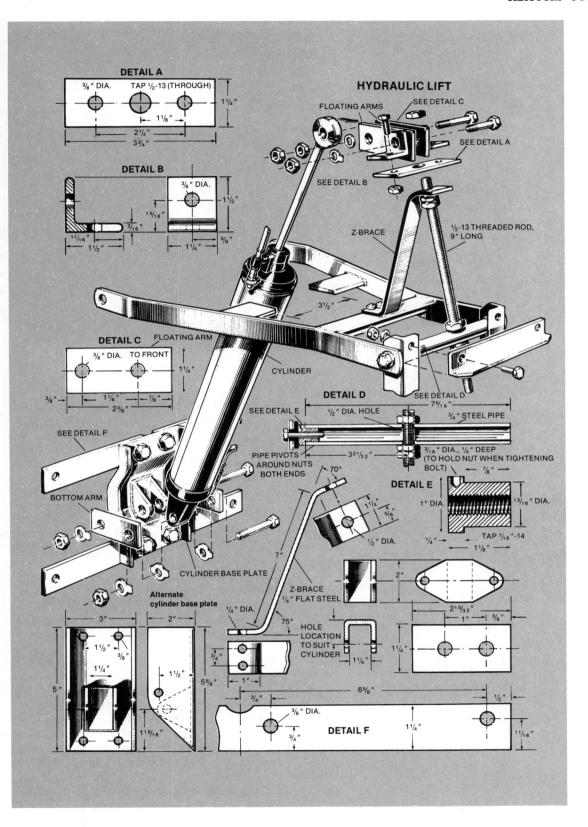

DETAIL A

³⁄₈″ DIA. TAP ½-13 (THROUGH)

1¼″

1⅛″

2¼″

3¾″

HYDRAULIC LIFT

FLOATING ARMS

SEE DETAIL C

SEE DETAIL A

SEE DETAIL B

Z-BRACE

½-13 THREADED ROD, 9″ LONG

DETAIL B

³⁄₈″ DIA.

1½″

1⁵⁄₁₆″

³⁄₁₆″

⁵⁄₈″

1½″

1¼″

3½″

DETAIL C FLOATING ARM

³⁄₈″ DIA. TO FRONT

1¼″

1⅛″ ⅞″

³⁄₈″

2⅜″

SEE DETAIL F

CYLINDER

SEE DETAIL D

7⁵⁄₁₆″

DETAIL D

SEE DETAIL E

½″ DIA. HOLE

¾″ STEEL PIPE

PIPE PIVOTS AROUND NUTS BOTH ENDS

3²¹⁄₃₂″

³⁄₁₆″ DIA., ¼″ DEEP (TO HOLD NUT WHEN TIGHTENING BOLT)

⅞″

70°

DETAIL E

BOTTOM ARM

1¼″

⁵⁄₈″

½″ DIA.

1″ DIA.

¼″

1⅛″

TAP ⁷⁄₁₆″-14

1³⁄₁₆″ DIA.

CYLINDER BASE PLATE

Alternate cylinder base plate

7″

Z-BRACE ¼″ FLAT STEEL

¼″ DIA.

75°

HOLE LOCATION TO SUIT CYLINDER

1¼″

1″

2″

2¹⁵⁄₃₂″

1″ ⁵⁄₈″

1¼″

3″

2″

1½″ ³⁄₈″

1¼″

5″

1½″

5⅝″

1¹⁵⁄₁₆″

¾″

1¼″

6⁵⁄₈″

½″

¾″

³⁄₈″ DIA.

DETAIL F

1¼″

¾″

1¹¹⁄₁₆″

CYLINDER BOTTOM arms are attached to plate with a bolt and to cylinder with shaft, washer and cotter pin.

BLADE RESTING on ground exposes ½-in. threaded rod. Extended down, it allows room for adjustment.

Finally, fasten the cylinder base to the upper and lower braces.

The cylinder came equipped with a base plate which was adaptable to this tractor when bottom arms were added. If this part is missing on the unit that you purchase, you can make the alternate base plate shown in the drawings. With this version, the bottom arms can be eliminated since the cylinder-holding U-channel provides ample swing-clearance.

The motor-pump reservoir unit fits snugly under the tractor hood. On this rig it had to be positioned on the top left side of the engine between the air cleaner, gas tank and left headlight. To make room, it was necessary to move the air-cleaner cover slightly to the right.

Current draw is given at about 35 amps, which is no problem for a 12-v. heavy-duty battery. The "on" time is very short since the blade is lifted at a speed of roughly 2 in. per second. If your blade doesn't stay up, due to slow leakage through the pump, it can be corrected by stiffening the pivot points of the upper and lower frames by inserting spring lock washers under the bolt heads.

All of the dimensions shown were determined by trial-and-error fitting. The lift shown was built to suit the tractor (Sears 10-hp XL). For other makes it is best to experiment with cardboard and/or plywood templates to check for fit and clearance before cutting, shaping and welding the iron.

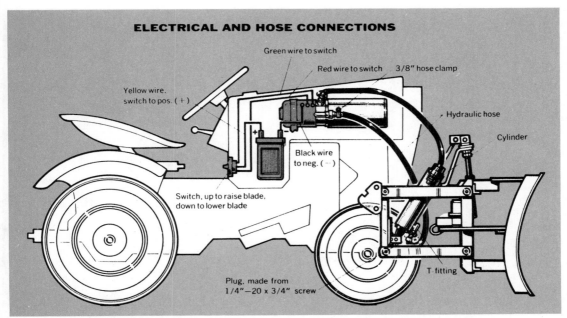

ELECTRICAL AND HOSE CONNECTIONS

Green wire to switch

Red wire to switch

3/8" hose clamp

Yellow wire, switch to pos. (+)

Hydraulic hose

Cylinder

Black wire to neg. (−)

Switch, up to raise blade, down to lower blade

Plug, made from 1/4"—20 x 3/4" screw

T-fitting

AFTER CUTTING HOSE to unused second cylinder, plug T-fitting with a ¼-in.-diameter bolt and a ⅜-in. clamp.

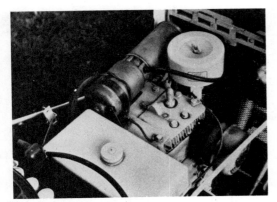

POWER UNIT fits neatly under hood on the engine's left side once the air cleaner has been moved slightly.

WITH THREADED ROD almost vertical, floating arm position indicates that the blade is free to float.

Garden tractor trailer

■ YOU'LL HAVE A SURE CURE for those backaches caused by heavy back-yard chores with this functional utility trailer that can be constructed of common materials to fit most any make of garden tractor.

The versatility of the trailer is mainly a result of the flexible arrangement of interlocking slatted sides and a removable rear panel. The trailer can be used with its four slatted sides, or it can be converted quickly to a three or four-sided flatbed type.

Made of four horizontal and two vertical strips of ¾ x 2¾-in. fir, the slatted sides slip into re-

tainers of 16-ga. cold-rolled steel (CRS) permanently mounted to the four side panels of ¾-in. exterior plywood. Attached to the top slats of each side are supports of 12-ga. CRS that hook onto each other and greatly strengthen the corner joints while allowing quick and easy removal of the sides without the need for any tools.

The main section of the trailer consists of a three-sided plywood enclosure mounted on a steel frame. The fourth side (rear panel) slips into the channel formed by the lengths of 1x1 and 2x2 angle that are screwed to the inner and outer surfaces of the side panels.

The frame or chassis of the trailer is made of 1⅛-in.-square steel bar, although steel pipe, square or round tubing, angle or channel also could be used. Regardless of which material you use, however, make certain that all joints are securely welded together with fillet welds.

Almost any type of pneumatic tire and wheel assembly can be used, as long as it is at least 12 in. in diameter. Suitable wheels often can be salvaged from wheelbarrows, boat trailers, golf

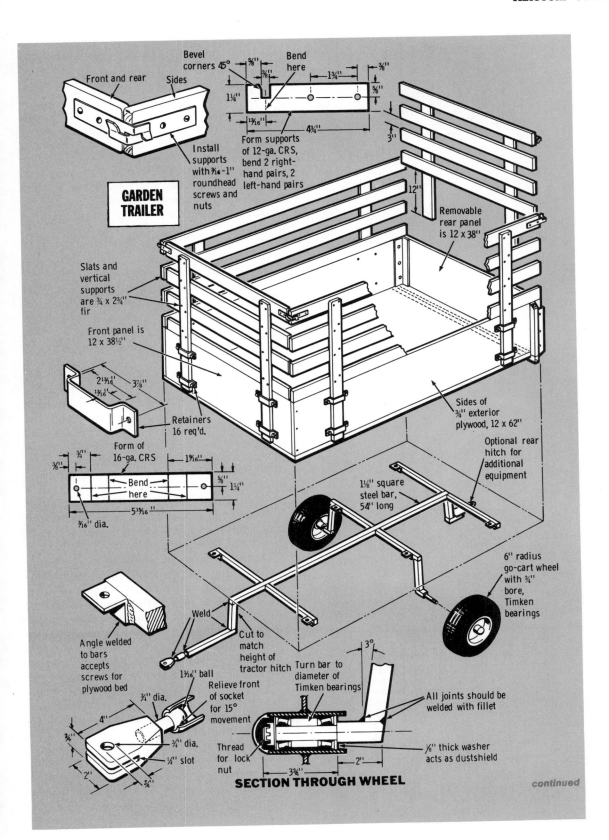

Front and rear

Sides

Install supports with ³⁄₁₆-1'' roundhead screws and nuts

GARDEN TRAILER

Bevel corners 45°

⁵⁄₈''

³⁄₈''

Bend here

1¾''

³⁄₈''

1¼''

⁵⁄₈''

1³⁄₁₆''

4¾''

3''

Form supports of 12-ga. CRS, bend 2 right-hand pairs, 2 left-hand pairs

12''

Removable rear panel is 12 x 38''

Slats and vertical supports are ¾ x 2¾'' fir

Front panel is 12 x 38½''

2¹³⁄₁₆''

3⁷⁄₈''

1³⁄₁₆''

Retainers 16 req'd.

Form of 16-ga. CRS

³⁄₄''

³⁄₈''

1³⁄₁₆''

Bend here

⁵⁄₈''

1¼''

5¹⁵⁄₁₆''

³⁄₁₆'' dia.

Sides of ¾'' exterior plywood, 12 x 62''

Optional rear hitch for additional equipment

1⅛'' square steel bar, 54'' long

6'' radius go-cart wheel with ¾'' bore, Timken bearings

Angle welded to bars accepts screws for plywood bed

Weld

Cut to match height of tractor hitch

1¹⁄₁₆'' ball

Relieve front of socket for 15° movement

³⁄₄'' dia.

4''

³⁄₄''

³⁄₄'' dia.

¼'' slot

2''

³⁄₄''

Thread for lock nut

Turn bar to diameter of Timken bearings

3°

All joints should be welded with fillet

⅛'' thick washer acts as dustshield

3¾''

2''

SECTION THROUGH WHEEL

continued

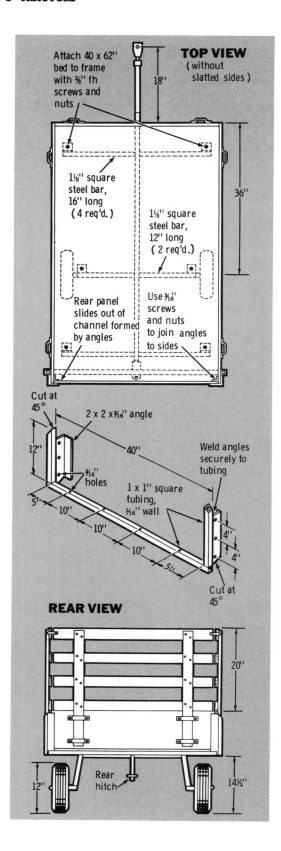

TOP VIEW
(without slatted sides)

Attach 40 x 62" bed to frame with ⅜" fh screws and nuts

18"

36"

1⅛" square steel bar, 16" long (4 req'd.)

1⅛" square steel bar, 12" long (2 req'd.)

Rear panel slides out of channel formed by angles

Use ¾6" screws and nuts to join angles to sides

Cut at 45°

2 x 2 x ¾6" angle

12"

40"

Weld angles securely to tubing

¾6" holes

1 x 1" square tubing, ¼6" wall

5" 10"

10"

10"

5"

4"

4"

Cut at 45°

REAR VIEW

20"

12"

Rear hitch

14½"

carts or lawnmowers. Go-kart wheels are probably the best choice, especially if they are equipped with tapered roller bearings. The inner diameter of the bearings should be at least ¾ in.

Ball bearings (sealed or nonsealed) or sleeve bearings will work equally well. However, provisions must be made for lubricating and sealing any hubs not fitted with sealed, prelubricated bearings.

The spindles are turned from the square steel bar to accommodate the wheels and bearings selected. The turned length should equal the spacing between bearings, plus the space required for a grease seal, flat washer and nut. The end of the turned spindle also can be threaded and drilled for a castellated nut and cotter pin.

An alternative method to form the spindles is to weld a headless bolt in a hole drilled in the supporting arm of the chassis. Be sure, however, that the wheel will clear the arm of the steel chassis.

Construction sequence

The steel frame and wheels should be assembled first, then fitted to your tractor so the proper vertical position of the hitch can be determined. The length of the horizontal bar connecting the hitch to the frame may also have to be modified slightly since the turning radius of your tractor might be smaller than that shown.

When completed and tested, the frame should be fitted with six short sections of angle drilled to facilitate the mounting of the bed to the frame. Then clean all welded areas, removing the slag completely, and give the frame a protective coat of zinc chromate primer.

The bed of the trailer is built upside down on a level surface. All joints should be made with waterproof glue and secured in alignment with 1¼-in. finishing nails. Then drill and drive in No. 8 1½-in. wood screws every 10 in. and allow the bed to dry before adding the U-support at the rear.

Six 3-in. blocks of scrap wood are used as spacers to insure the proper positioning of the slats on the vertical supports. Make certain the vertical supports are spaced the same distance away from the ends of the slats before gluing and screwing the sides together.

When all glued joints have dried, screw the bed to the frame. Then secure the retainers to the side panels and the locking supports to the corners of the slatted sides. Finish by painting and trimming the trailer to match the tractor's colors.

SHOP GUIDE

CUSTOMARY TO METRIC (CONVERSION) Conversion factors can be carried so far they become impractical. In cases below where an entry is exact it is followed by an asterisk (*). Where considerable rounding off has taken place, the entry is followed by a + or a − sign.

Linear Measure

inches	millimeters
1/16	1.5875*
1/8	3.2
3/16	4.8
1/4	6.35*
5/16	7.9
3/8	9.5
7/16	11.1
1/2	12.7*
9/16	14.3
5/8	15.9
11/16	17.5
3/4	19.05*
13/16	20.6
7/8	22.2
15/16	23.8
1	25.4*

inches	centimeters
1	2.54*
2	5.1
3	7.6
4	10.2
5	12.7*
6	15.2
7	17.8
8	20.3
9	22.9
10	25.4*
11	27.9
12	30.5

feet	centimeters	meters
1	30.48*	.3048*
2	61	.61
3	91	.91
4	122	1.22
5	152	1.52
6	183	1.83
7	213	2.13
8	244	2.44
9	274	2.74
10	305	3.05
50	1524*	15.24*
100	3048*	30.48*

1 yard = .9144* meters
1 rod = 5.0292* meters
1 mile = 1.6 kilometers
1 nautical mile = 1.852* kilometers

Weights

ounces	grams
1	28.3
2	56.7
3	85
4	113
5	142
6	170
7	198
8	227
9	255
10	283
11	312
12	340
13	369
14	397
15	425
16	454

Formula (exact):
ounces × 28.349 523 125* = grams

pounds	kilograms
1	.45
2	.9
3	1.4
4	1.8
5	2.3
6	2.7
7	3.2
8	3.6
9	4.1
10	4.5

1 short ton (2000 lbs) = 907 kilograms (kg)
Formula (exact):
pounds × .453 592 37* = kilograms

Fluid Measure

(Milliliters [ml] and cubic centimeters [cc] are equivalent, but it is customary to use milliliters for liquids.)

1 cu in	=	16.39 ml
1 fl oz	=	29.6 ml
1 cup	=	237 ml
1 pint	=	473 ml
1 quart	=	946 ml
	=	.946 liters
1 gallon	=	3785 ml
	=	3.785 liters

Formula (exact):
fluid ounces × 29.573 529 562 5* = milliliters

Volume

1 cu in	=	16.39 cubic centimeters (cc)
1 cu ft	=	28 316.7 cc
1 bushel	=	35 239.1 cc
1 peck	=	8 809.8 cc

Area

1 sq in	=	6.45 sq cm
1 sq ft	=	929 sq cm
	=	.093 sq meters
1 sq yd	=	.84 sq meters
1 acre	=	4 046.9 sq meters
	=	.404 7 hectares
1 sq mile	=	2 589 988 sq meters
	=	259 hectares
	=	2.589 9 sq kilometers

Miscellaneous

1 British thermal unit (Btu) (mean) = 1 055.9 joules
1 horsepower = 745.7 watts
= .75 kilowatts
caliber (diameter of a firearm's bore in hundredths of an inch) = .254 millimeters (mm)

1 atmosphere pressure = 101 325* pascals (newtons per sq meter)
1 pound per square inch (psi) = 6 895 pascals
1 pound per square foot = 47.9 pascals
1 knot = 1.85 kilometers per hour
1 mile per hour = 1.6093 kilometers per hour